SOLUTIONS MANUAL

to accompany

GENERAL STATISTICS

WARREN CHASE
FRED BOWN
Framingham State College

JOHN WILEY & SONS
New York Chichester Brisbane Toronto Singapore

Authors' note: Due to rounding procedures, some of the readers' answers may differ from those in the manual.

1.1   A sample is a subset of a population, so that they have common elements. However, a population may contain elements which are not part of a sample.

1.2   A parameter and a statistic are numerical properties of a collection of elements. A parameter is a fixed value, whereas the value of a statistic varies from sample to sample.

1.3   True

1.4   True

1.5   False

1.6   Descriptive

1.7   Inferential

1.8   Descriptive

1.9   Descriptive

1.10   Parameter

1.11   Statistic

1.12   Statistic

1.13   (a)   The population is the collection of 750 seniors. There are 750 data values in the population.

        (b)   The average GPA.

        (c) $\frac{27.1}{10} = 2.71$

        (d)   No. The two samples would consist of different data values and most likely the average values would be different. However, the value of the parameter would remain the same.

1.14 (a) The collection of 10000 voters.

(b) 0.35

(c) 0.40

(d) It is not surprising that the answers in parts (b) and (c) differ, as they are based on different collections of data values. The value of the statistic would most likely change if another sample were taken.

1.15 (a) A family is an element of the population. The population size is 1000.

(b) The sample size is 50.

(c) (i) $8 + 6 + 8 = 22$
(ii) $300 + 80 + 50 = 430$

(d) (i) $\dfrac{6 + 10 + 12 + 8}{50} = 0.72$

(ii) $\dfrac{120 + 180 + 270 + 300}{1000} = 0.87$

2.1   (a)

x	1	4	6	9	10	12
f	5	5	3	1	2	4

(b)   Use 20 distinct data values.

2.2   (a)

x	0	1	2	3	4
f	6	7	4	2	1

(b)   3/20

2.3

State (x)	Frequency (f)
Maine	16000
New Hampshire	14000
Vermont	8000
Massachusetts	66000
Rhode Island	11000
Connecticut	34000

2.4   (a)

x	46	49	50	53	54	55	57	58	59	60	62	63	64
f	1	1	1	1	1	2	1	1	2	1	1	1	1

x	65	66	68	69	70	71	72	73	74	76	78	79	80
f	2	4	2	1	1	2	1	3	1	1	1	1	1

x	82	83	84	88
f	1	1	1	1

(b)   The frequency distribution does not help much in simplifying the data, as there are too many distinct data values.

2.5

Class Limits	Class Frequency f
45-59	11
60-74	21
75-89	8

Class width = 60 − 45 = 15

2.6

Class Limits	Class Frequency f
45-48	1
49-52	2
53-56	4
57-60	5
61-64	3
65-68	8
69-72	5
73-76	5
77-80	3
81-84	3
85-88	1

Class width = 49−45 = 4

2.7

Class Limits	Class Frequency f
46-48	1
49-51	2
52-54	2
55-57	3
58-60	4
61-63	2
64-66	7
67-69	3
70-72	4
73-75	4
76-78	2
79-81	2
82-84	3
85-87	0
88-90	1

Class width
= 49-46 = 3

2.9   The class mark for a particular class is the number located halfway between the class limits (or halfway between the class boundaries).

The class mark can be found by one-half the sum of the class limits (or by one-half the sum of the class boundaries).

2.10   (a)

Class Limits	Class Boundaries	Class Mark
61-63	60.5-63.5	62
64-66	63.5-66.5	65
67-69	66.5-69.5	68
70-72	69.5-72.5	71
73-75	72.5-75.5	74
76-78	75.5-78.5	77
79-81	78.5-81.5	80
82-84	81.5-84.5	83

(b)

Class Limits	Class Boundaries	Class Mark
61-62	60.5-62.5	61.5
63-64	62.5-64.5	63.5
65-66	64.5-66.5	65.5
67-68	66.5-68.5	67.5
69-70	68.5-70.5	69.5
71-72	70.5-72.5	71.5
73-74	72.5-74.5	73.5
75-76	74.5-76.5	75.5
77-78	76.5-78.5	77.5
79-80	78.5-80.5	79.5
81-82	80.5-82.5	81.5
83-84	82.5-84.5	83.5

2.11 (a)

Class	Class Limits	Class Boundaries	Class Mark
1	87.9-89.1	87.85-89.15	88.5
2	89.2-90.4	89.15-90.45	89.8
3	90.5-91.7	90.45-91.75	91.1
4	91.8-93.0	91.75-93.05	92.4
5	93.1-94.3	93.05-94.35	93.7

(b)

Class	Class Limits	Class Boundaries	Class Mark
1	87.9-88.4	87.85-88.45	88.15
2	88.5-89.0	88.45-89.05	88.75
3	89.1-89.6	89.05-89.65	89.35
4	89.7-90.2	89.65-90.25	89.95
5	90.3-90.8	90.25-90.85	90.55
6	90.9-91.4	90.85-91.45	91.15
7	91.5-92.0	91.45-92.05	91.75
8	92.1-92.6	92.05-92.65	92.35
9	92.7-93.2	92.65-93.25	92.95
10	93.3-93.8	93.25-93.85	93.55
11	93.9-94.4	93.85-94.45	94.15

2.12 (a)

Class	Class Boundaries	Frequency	Cumulative Frequency
1	189.75-196.75	5	5
2	196.75-203.75	2	7
3	203.75-210.75	9	16
4	210.75-217.75	4	20
5	217.75-224.75	6	26
6	224.75-231.75	3	29
7	231.75-238.75	1	30

(b) $(203.75 + 210.75)/2 = 207.25$ (c) $196.75 - 189.75 = 7$

2.13 (a)

Class	Class Boundaries	Frequency	Cumulative Frequency
1	152.5-171.5	1	1
2	171.5-190.5	3	4
3	190.5-209.5	6	10
4	209.5-228.5	5	15
5	228.5-247.5	7	22
6	247.5-266.5	3	25
7	266.5-285.5	5	30
8	285.5-304.5	5	35

(b) $(209.5 + 228.5)/2 = 219$ (c) $171.5 - 152.5 = 19$

(d) $6/35 = 0.17$

2.14 (a)

Class	Class Limits	Frequency
1	15-17	2
2	18-20	5
3	21-23	3
4	24-26	12
5	27-29	4
6	30-32	4

(b) 18-15 = 3   (c) 14.5   (d) 5/30 = 1/6

(e) 20/30 = 2/3

2.15 (a)

Class	Class Limits	Class Mark	Frequency	Cumulative Frequency
1	34- 310	172	20	20
2	311- 587	449	18	38
3	588- 864	726	5	43
4	865-1141	1003	2	45
5	1142-1418	1280	1	46
6	1419-1695	1557	2	48
7	1696-1972	1834	1	49
8	1973-2249	2111	1	50

(b) 311-34 = 277   (c) 16

2.18 (a)   (b)

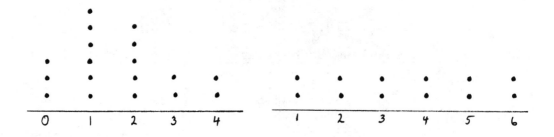

2.19   (a)

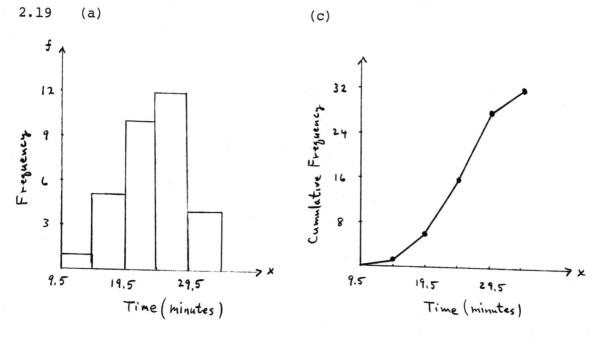

(c)

(b)

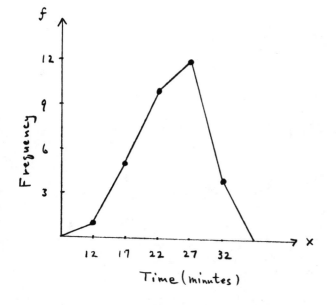

(d) Class width = 15 – 10 = 5

2.20   (a)

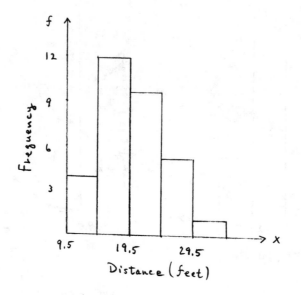

(b)

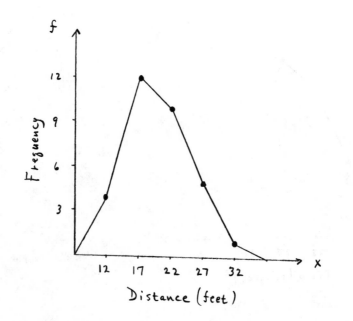

2.20   (c)

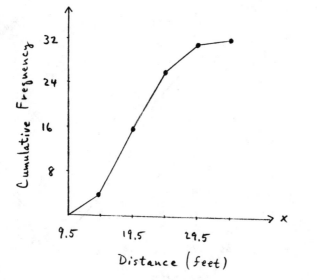

(d)   Class width
        15-10 = 5

2.21   (a)

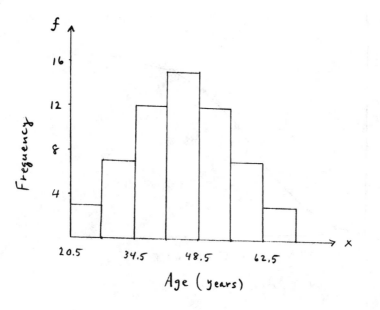

9

2.21   (b)

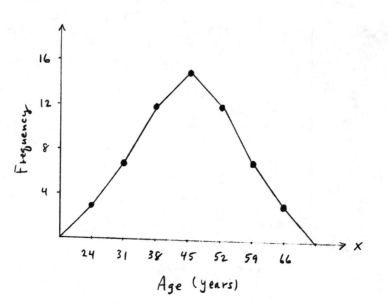

2.21   (c)   (d)   Class Width
                                                    = 28-21 = 7

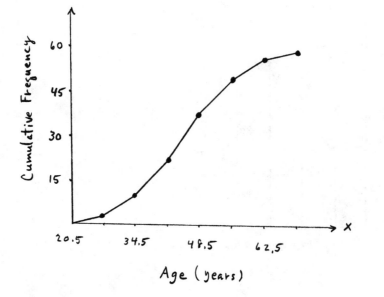

2.22　(a)

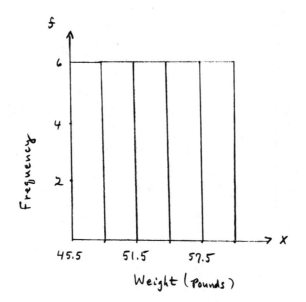

(b)

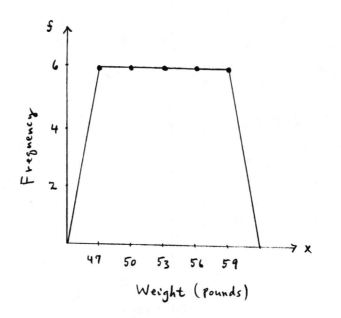

2.22   (c)   (d)   Class width
                                                                = 49-46 = 3

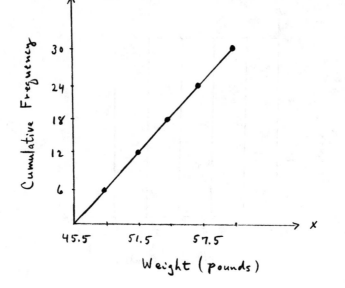

Weight (pounds)

2.23   (a)

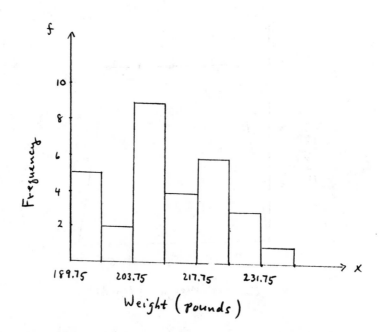

Weight (pounds)

2.23　　(b)

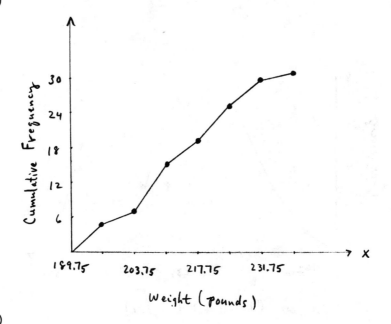

2.24　　(a)

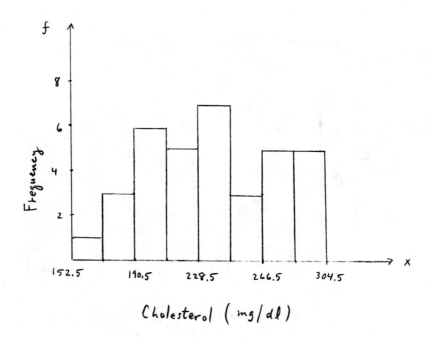

13

2.24   (b)

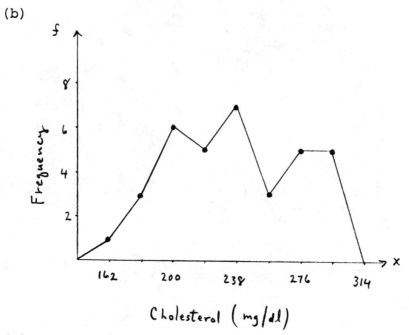

(c)

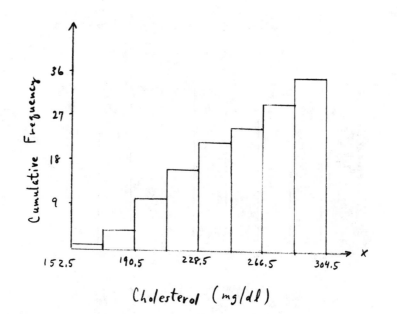

2.24   (d)

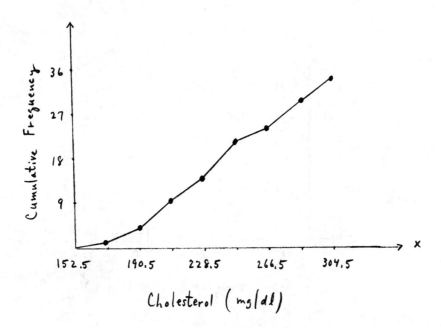

Cholesterol (mg/dl)

2.25　　(a)

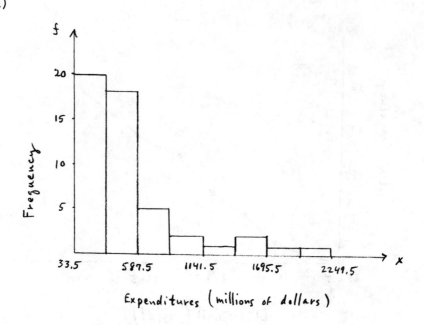

Expenditures (millions of dollars)

(b)

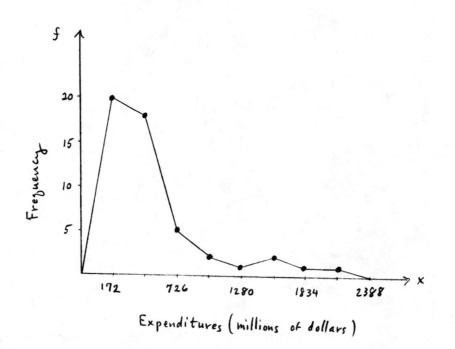

Expenditures (millions of dollars)

16

2.25   (c)

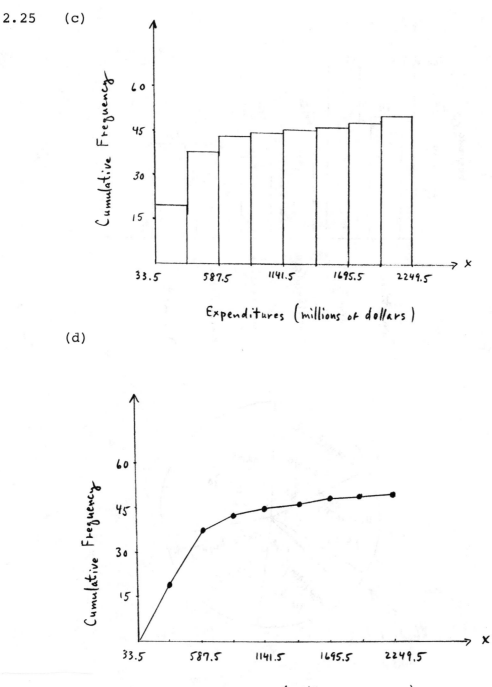

Expenditures (millions of dollars)

(d)

Expenditures (millions of dollars)

2.26　(a)

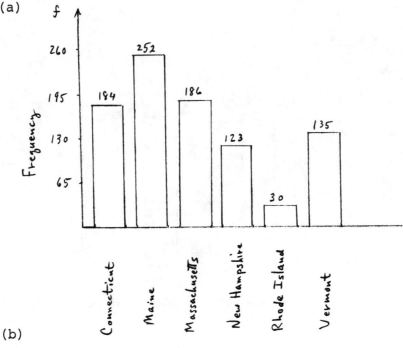

(b)

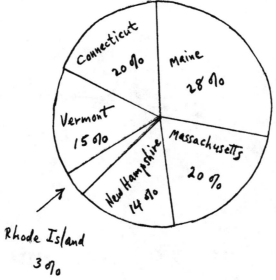

2.27   (a)

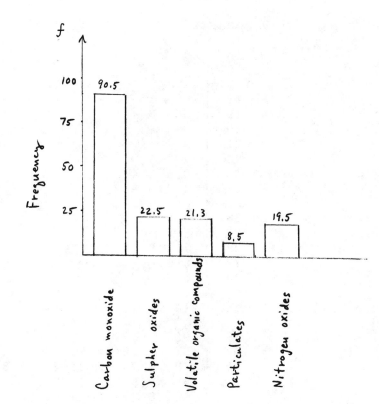

(b)

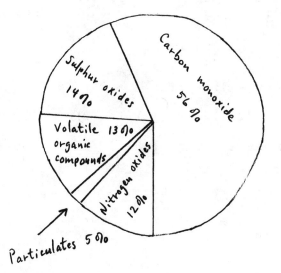

2.28   For example, 28|7 means 287

```
15 | 6
16 |
17 | 2
18 | 2 5
19 | 5 8 8
20 | 0 4 4
21 | 5 7
22 | 4 8 1
23 | 0 6 4 4
24 | 2 4 4
25 | 6
26 | 0 5 7
27 | 8 8
28 | 7 1 0
29 | 8 1
30 | 0 2
```

2.29   For example, 21|49 means 214.9

```
18 | 98
19 | 84 42 29 64 59
20 | 40 51 76 82 84 21 38 89 63
21 | 49 59 95 29 06 69
22 | 26 28 22 00 24 80 85
23 | 09 59
```

2.30   (2.19) skewed to the left   (2.20) skewed to the right
       (2.21) bell shaped   (2.22) uniform

2.31   (a)

x	0	1	2	3	4	5
f	30	60	45	12	2	1

       (b)   30 + 60 + 45 + 12 + 2 + 1 = 150

       (c)   1(60) + 2(45) + 3(12) + 4(2) + 5(1) = 199

       (d)   at least 1 hit: (150-30)/150 = 120/150

             at least 3 hits: (12 + 2 + 1)/150 = 15/150

             no more than 1 hit: (30 + 60)/150 = 90/150

       (e)   False: The proportion of times he had at least 2
             hits is (45 + 12 + 2 + 1)/150 = 60/150.

2.32

x	0	1	2	3	4	5
f	2	2	6	6	2	2

2.33   For each variable, most data values occur with frequency
        one. In each case, it would not be worthwhile to construct
        a frequency distribution.

2.34   The proportion of females sampled is 16/20. It does not
        seem representative.

2.35

Class	Class Limits	Class Frequency f
1	0- 6	3
2	7-13	4
3	14-20	4
4	21-27	5
5	28-34	4

2.36   (a)

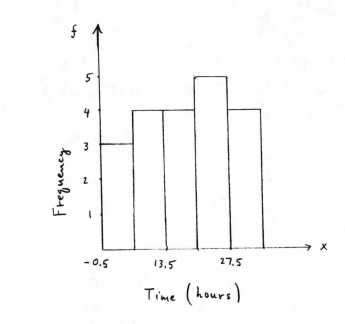

(b)

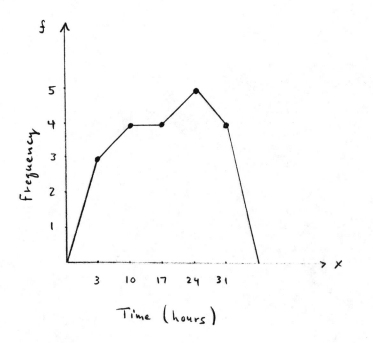

2.37

Class	Class Limits	Class Frequency f
1	19-29	4
2	30-40	6
3	41-51	2
4	52-62	2
5	63-73	4
6	74-84	2

2.38   (a)

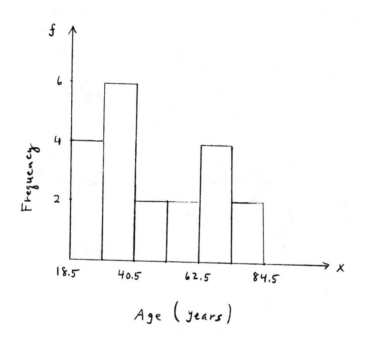

Age (years)

2.38   (b)

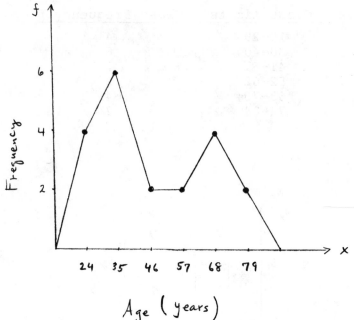

Age (years)

2.39

			Relative	Cumulative
Class	Class Boundaries	Frequency	Frequency	Frequency
1	3.5- 6.5	10	0.05	10
2	6.5- 9.5	30	0.15	40
3	9.5-12.5	12	0.06	52
4	12.5-15.5	47	0.235	99
5	15.5-18.5	50	0.25	149
6	18.5-21.5	28	0.14	177
7	21.5-24.5	5	0.025	182
8	24.5-27.5	18	0.09	200
Total		200		

(a)   (50 + 28 + 5 + 18)/200 = 101/200   (b)   47/200

2.40   (a)   We used columns three and four of the random number
              table.

```
  .               .   .
  .     .         .   .
  .     .     .     .     .             .   .   .
  .     .     .   .   .   .   .         .   .   .
  .     .     .   .   .   .   .   .     .   .   .
  .     .     .   .   .   .   .   .   . .   .   .
─────────────────────────────────────────────────────
  0     1     2   3   4   5   6   7   8   9
```

       (b)   Each integer should occur about 1/10 of the time.   The
              approximate shape of the distribution should be
              uniform.

24

2.41

Class	Class Limits	Class Boundaries	Class Mark	Frequency	Relative Frequency	Cumulative Frequency	Cumulative Relative Frequency
1	0.9-1.5	0.85-1.55	1.2	5	0.10	5	0.10
2	1.6-2.2	1.55-2.25	1.9	8	0.16	13	0.26
3	2.3-2.9	2.25-2.95	2.6	13	0.26	26	0.52
4	3.0-3.6	2.95-3.65	3.3	15	0.30	41	0.82
5	3.7-4.3	3.65-4.35	4.0	6	0.12	47	0.94
6	4.4-5.0	4.35-5.05	4.7	2	0.04	49	0.98
7	5.1-5.7	5.05-5.75	5.4	0	0.00	49	0.98
8	5.8-6.4	5.75-6.45	6.1	1	0.02	50	1.00

Class width = 1.6 - 0.9 = 0.7

2.42   (a)

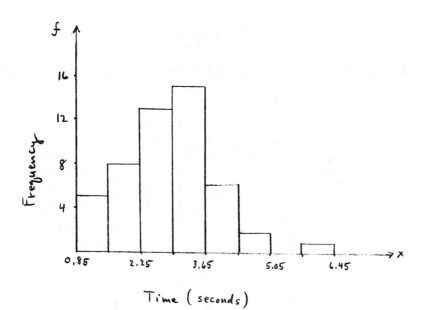

Time (seconds)

2.42   (b)

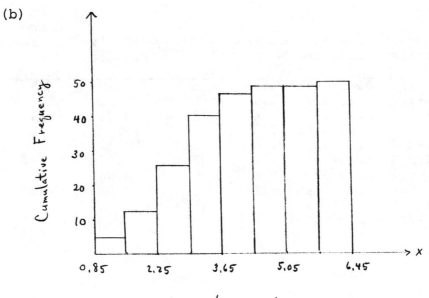

Time (seconds)

2.43

Class	Class Limits	Frequency	Cumulative Frequency
1	0.9-1.3	3	3
2	1.4-1.8	7	10
3	1.9-2.3	5	15
4	2.4-2.8	10	25
5	2.9-3.3	11	36
6	3.4-3.8	10	46
7	3.9-4.3	1	47
8	4.4-4.8	2	49
9	4.9-5.3	0	49
10	5.4-5.8	0	49
11	5.9-6.3	0	49
12	6.4-6.8	1	50

2.44   (a)

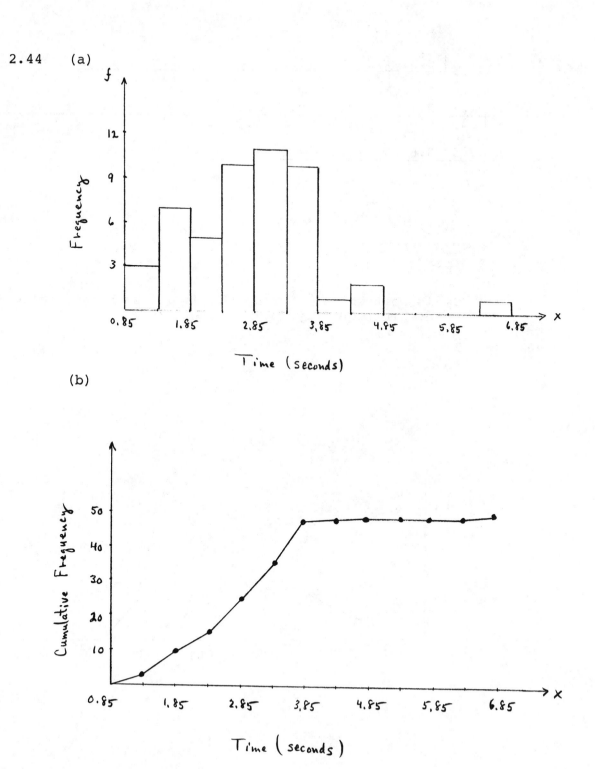

(b)

2.45 (a)

x	0.9	1.3	1.4	1.5	1.6	1.7	1.8	2.0	2.1	2.2
f	1	2	1	1	2	2	1	1	1	1

x	2.3	2.4	2.5	2.6	2.7	2.8	2.9	3.0	3.1	3.2	3.3	3.4
f	2	1	1	3	3	2	1	1	3	2	4	3

x	3.5	3.6	3.7	3.8	4.0	4.5	6.4
f	1	1	3	2	1	2	1

(b)

(c) It is worthwhile to group the data. Each data value occurs infrequently.

2.46 (a)

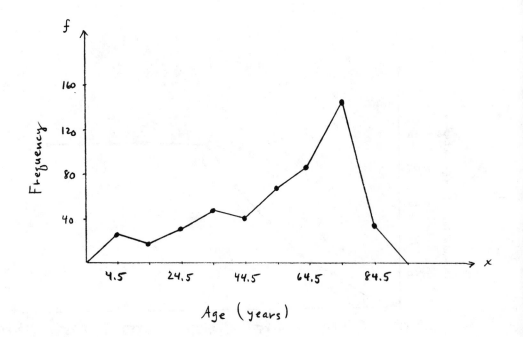

Age (years)

2.46   (b)

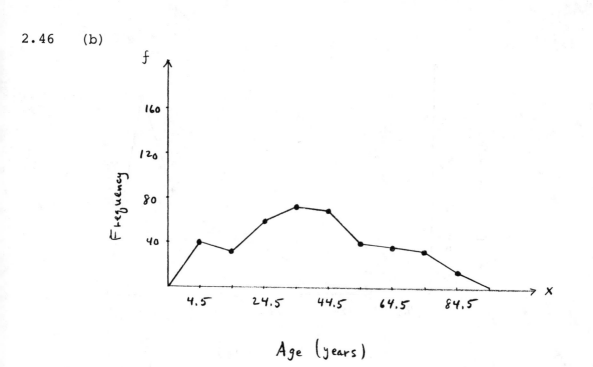

Age (years)

(c)   The number at the Florida hospital is much larger
      than that at the Massachusetts hospital after age 45

2.47   (a)

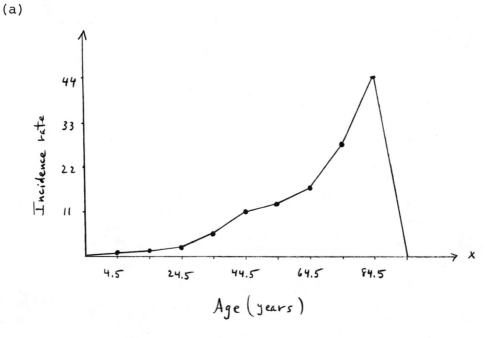

Age (years)

2.47   (b)

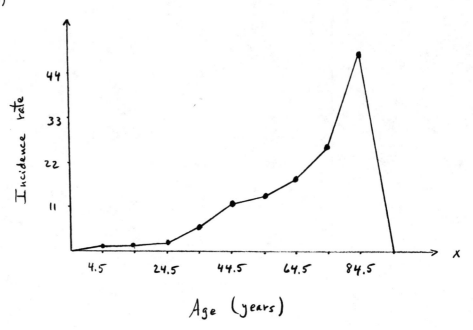

Age (years)

(c)   There appears to be little difference between the
states relative to hospital admittance.

2.48   (a)

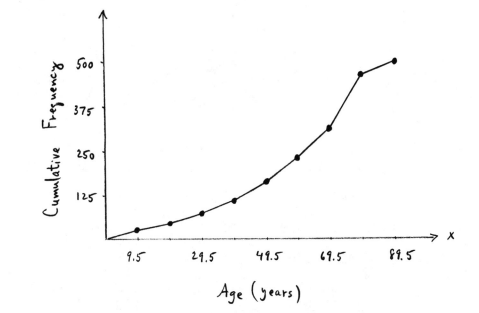

Age (years)

(b)

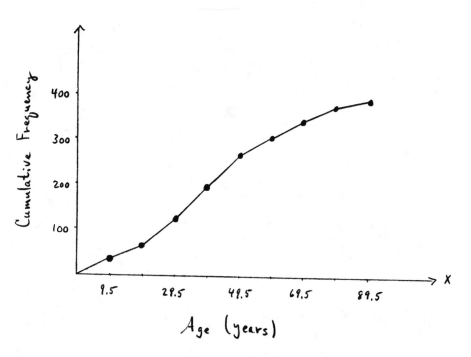

Age (years)

2.50	Age at Admittance	Number at Florida (f) Hospital	Cumulative Frequency
	0- 9	27	27
	10-19	19	46
	20-29	31	77
	30-39	47	124
	40-49	42	166
	50-59	68	234
	60-69	87	321
	70-79	145	466
	80-89	34	500

(a) $500 - 124 = 376$ (b) 321 (c) $466 - 77 = 389$

2.51   (a) $42 + 68 + 87 + 145 + 34 = 376$

(b) $500 - (145 + 34) = 321$

(c) $47 + 42 + 68 + 87 + 145 = 389$

2.52

Age at Admittance	Cumulative Relative Frequency
0- 9	0.054
10-19	0.092
20-29	0.154
30-39	0.248
40-49	0.332
50-59	0.468
60-69	0.642
70-79	0.932
80-89	1.000

(a) $1.000 - 0.248 = 0.752$ (b) 0.642

(c) $0.932 - 0.154 = 0.778$

2.53

Class	Class Limits	Frequency 1970	Frequency 1980
1	2209- 9381	16	8
2	9382-16554	6	13
3	16555-23727	4	4
4	23728-30900	2	3
5	30901-38073	0	0
6	38074-45246	0	0
7	45247-52419	0	0
8	52420-59592	1	0
9	59593-66765	0	0
10	66766-73938	0	1
11	73939-81111	0	0
12	81112-88284	1	0
13	88285-95457	0	1

2.54   (a)

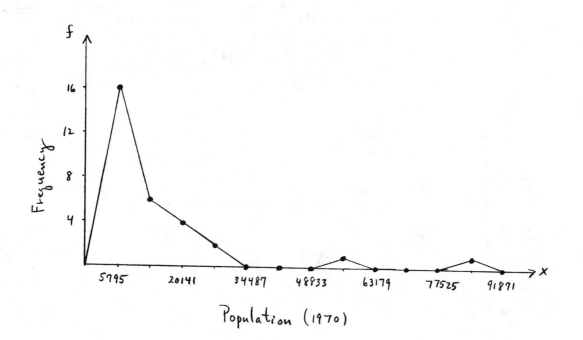

Population (1970)

.54 (b)

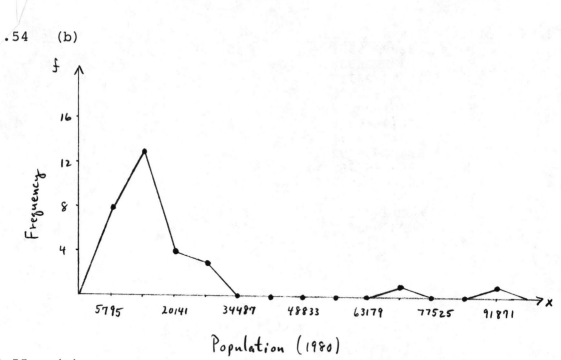

Population (1980)

2.55 (a)

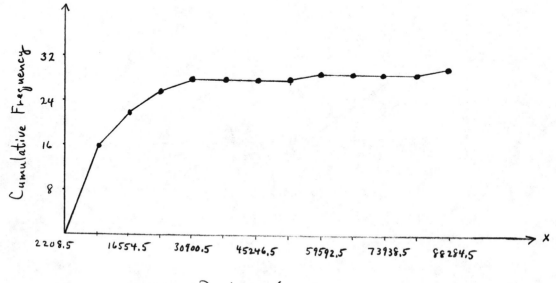

Population (1970)

2.55 (b)

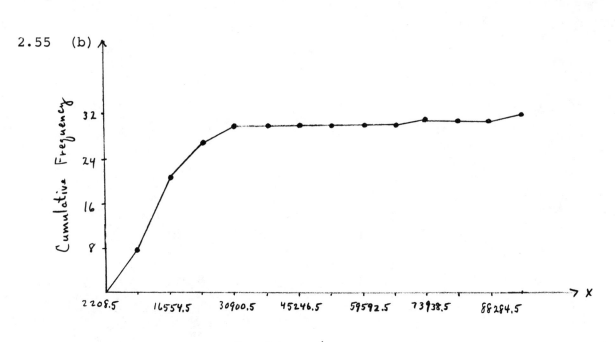

Population (1980)

2.56

Class	Class Limits	Class Frequency f (1975)	Class Frequency f (1982)
	88- 629	25	27
	630-1171	13	15
	1172-1713	5	1
	1714-2255	2	4
	2256-2797	2	1
	2798-3339	1	1
	3340-3881	1	0
	3882-4423	1	1

2.57   (a)

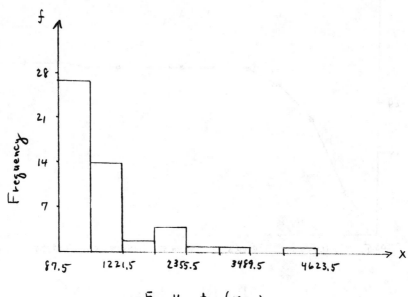

Enrollments (1975)

(b)

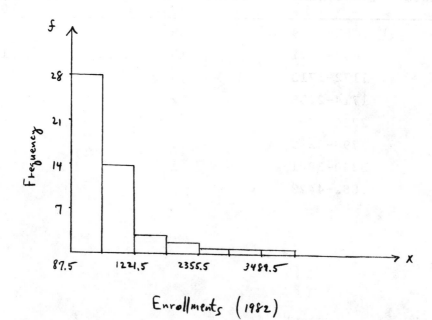

Enrollments (1982)

36

2.58   (a)

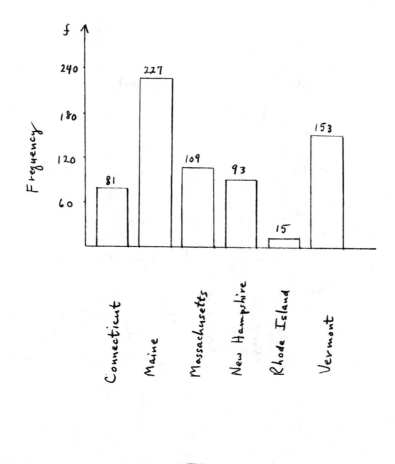

(b)

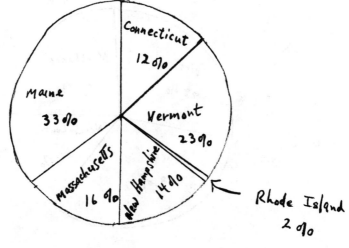

2.59   (a)

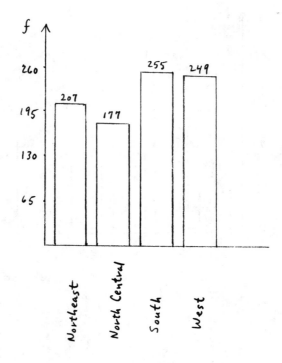

(b)

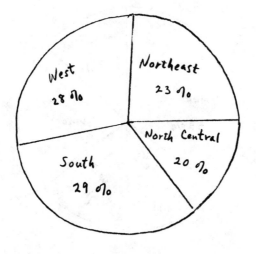

2.60
```
1 | 9
2 | 9 6 4
3 | 0 1 2 0 8
4 | 7 7 0
5 | 3 5
6 | 3 6 8
7 | 1 4
8 | 2
```

2.61

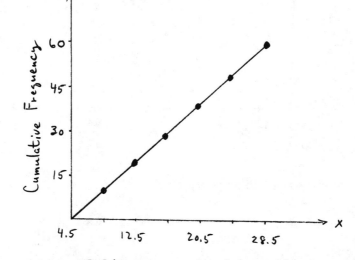

The sequence of line segments form a line.

2.62

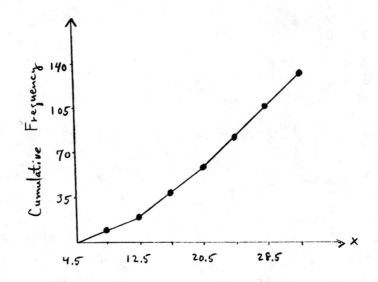

There are three line segments.

2.63   (a)

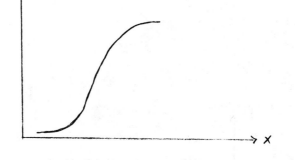

(b)

(c)

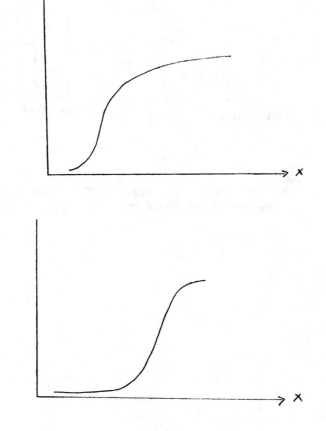

2.64

More	Same	Less
1962	1963	1965
1964		1966
1968		1967

2.65   (a)

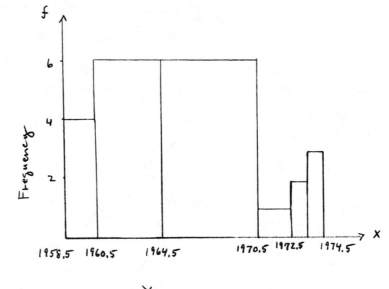

No, because the areas of the rectangles are not propor-
tional to the frequency of the appropriate class.

2.65   (b)

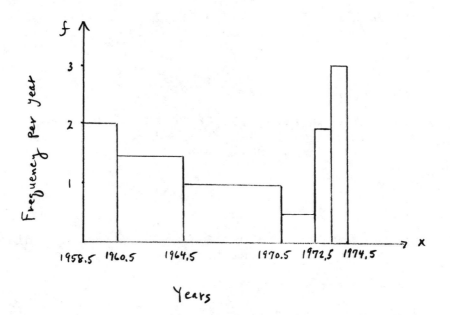

The frequency histogram in part (b) gives a more
accurate description of profits.

3.1   (a) $\bar{x} = \sum x/n = 48/6 = 8$

       (b)   Ranked data: 2,6,7,9,12,12   Location of median
             = (6 + 1)/2 = 3.5, so that median = (7 + 9)/2 = 8

       (c)   mode = 12

3.2   (a) $\bar{x} = \sum x/n = 1032/12 = 86$

       (b)   Ranked data: 74,74,78,80,80,84,90,90,92,94,98,98
             Location of median = (12 + 1)/2 = 6.5, so that
             median = (84 + 90)/2 = 87

       (c)   no mode

3.3   (a) $\bar{x} = \sum x/n = 16/5 = 3.2$

       (b)   Ranked data: 0,0,4,5,7   Location of median
             = (5 + 1)/2 = 3, so that median = 4

       (c)   mode = 0

3.4   (a) $\bar{x} = \sum x/n = 140/7 = 20$

       (b)   Ranked data: 14,16,17,19,19,21,34
             Location of median = (7 + 1)/2 = 4, so that median = 19

       (c)   mode = 19

3.5   (a) $\bar{x} = \sum x/n = 78.9/10 = 7.89$

       (b)   Ranked data: 6.4,7.1,7.4,7.6,7.6,7.6,8.3,8.5,9.0,9.4
             Location of median = (10 + 1)/2 = 5.5, so that
             median = (7.6 + 7.6)/2 = 7.6

       (c)   mode = 7.6

3.6   (a) $\bar{x} = \sum x/n = 50/5 = 10$

       (b)   Ranked data: 7,8,10,12,13   Location of median
             = (5 + 1)/2 = 3, so that median = 10

       (c)   no mode

3.7   (a) $\bar{x} = \sum x/n = 1159/15 = 77.27$

       (b) Ranked data: 66,67,69,71,72,74,75,78,79,82,82,83,
            85,87,89
            Location of median = (15 + 1)/2 = 8, so that median = 78

       (c) mode = 82

3.8   (a) $\bar{x} = \sum x/n = 153/6 = 25.5$

       (b) Ranked data: 23.1, 24.0, 24.2, 25.7, 26.3, 29.7
            Location of median = (6 + 1)/2 = 3.5, so that
            median = (24.2 + 25.7)/2 = 24.95

       (c) no mode

3.9   (a)

Class Limits	Frequency f	Class Mark X	Xf
9-17	14	13	182
18-26	9	22	198
27-35	7	31	217
36-44	4	40	160
45-53	3	49	147
54-62	1	58	58
Sum = 38			Sum = 962

$\bar{x} \doteq \sum Xf/n = 962/38 = 25.32$

       (b)

Class Limits	Frequency f	Class Mark X	Xf
9-17	1	13	13
18-26	3	22	66
27-35	4	31	124
36-44	7	40	280
45-53	9	49	441
54-62	14	58	812
Sum = 38			Sum = 1736

$\bar{x} \doteq \sum Xf/n = 1736/38 = 45.68$

3.10   Ranked data: 2,4,5,6,9
       Location of median = (5 + 1)/2 = 3, so that median = 5

3.11   Ranked data: 2,6,7,9,12,12
       Location of median = (6 + 1)/2 = 3.5, so that
       median = (7 + 9)/2 = 8

3.12   False. See exercise 3.11.

3.13   The student did not rank the data.

3.14   About half of the four-person families in the United
        States in 1977 reported an income of less than $18723.

3.15   (a)   Ranked data:
               16605, 17123, 18033, 18632, 18642, 18714, 19485,
               20053, 20591, 21860
               Location of median = $(10 + 1)/2 = 5.5$, so that
               median = $(18642 + 18714)/2 = 18678$.

        (b) $\bar{x} = \sum x/n = 189738/10 = 18973.8$

3.16   (a) $\sum x = 2 + 5 + 2 + 6 + 0 = 15$

        (b) $\sum (x - \bar{x}) = (2 - 3) + (5 - 3) + (2 - 3) + (6 - 3) + (0 - 3) = 0$

        (c) $\sum (x - \bar{x})^2 = (2-3)^2 + (5-3)^2 + (2-3)^2 + (6-3)^2 + (3-0)^2 = 24$

        (d) $\sum x^2 = (2)^2 + (5)^2 + (2)^2 + (6)^2 + (0)^2 = 69$

        (e) $(\sum x)^2 = (15)^2 = 225$

        (f) $\sum 7x = 7(2) + 7(5) + 7(2) + 7(6) + 7(0) = 105$

               $7\sum x = 7(15) = 105$

3.17   (a) $\bar{x} = \sum x/n = 355/20 = 17.75$

        (b)   Ranked data:
               3,3,4,7,11,12,13,16,17,18,19,21,21,23,24,27,28,28,
               29,31.
               Location of median = $(20 + 1)/2 = 10.5$, so that
               median = $(18 + 19)/2 = 18.5$

        (c)   no mode

        (d)   The mean and median seem to do equally well.

3.18   (a) $\bar{x} = \sum x/n = 50/20 = 2.5$

        (b)   Ranked data:
               0,0,1,1,2,2,2,2,2,2,3,3,3,3,3,3,4,4,5,5
               Location of median = $(20 + 1)/2 = 10.5$, so that
               median = $(2 + 3)/2 = 2.5$

        (c)   no mode

        (d)   The mean and median are equal in value.

3.19　(a)

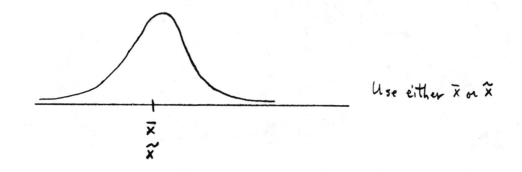

Use either $\bar{x}$ or $\tilde{x}$

$\bar{x}$
$\tilde{x}$

(b)

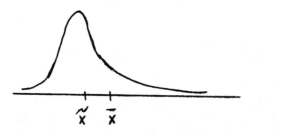

Use $\tilde{x}$

$\tilde{x}$　$\bar{x}$

(c)

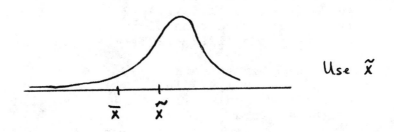

Use $\tilde{x}$

$\bar{x}$　$\tilde{x}$

3.20 (a) $\bar{x} = \sum x/n = 948/12 = 79$

(b) Ranked data:
75,76,77,77,78,79,79,80,80,81,81,85
Location of median = $(12 + 1)/2 = 6.5$, so that
median = $(79 + 79)/2 = 79$

(c) no mode

3.21 (a) $\bar{x} = \sum x/n = 14/7 = 2$

(b) Ranked data: 0,0,0,2,3,4,5   Location of median
= $(7 + 1)/2 = 4$, so that median = 2

(c) 0

3.22 (a) $\bar{x} = \sum x/n = 12679/7 = 1811.29$

(b) Ranked data: 328,710,827,972,1158,2214,6470
Location of median = $(7+1)/2=4$, so that median = 972

(c) Median. Note the effect of the extreme value 6470
on the mean.

3.23 (a) $\bar{x} = \sum x/n = 60272/8 = 7534$

(b) Ranked data:
5156, 6202, 6991, 7406, 7637, 7929, 8273, 10678
Location of median = $(8+1)/2 = 4.5$, so that
median = $(7406 + 7637)/2 = 7521.5$

3.24 (a) Boston: $\bar{x} = \sum x/n = 150.6/12 = 12.55$
Chicago: $\bar{x} = \sum x/n = 123.3/12 = 10.28$

(b) Boston: Ranked data:
10.7,10.9,11.3,11.4,12.0,12.2,12.9,13.3,13.7,13.9,
14.1,14.2   Location of median = $(12+1)/2 = 6.5$, so
that median = $(12.2 + 12.9)/2 = 12.55$

Chicago: Ranked data:
8.1,8.1,8.7,9.1,9.8,10.6,10.9,10.9,11.5,11.6,11.9,12.1
Location of median=$(12+1)/2=6.5$, so that
median = $(10.6 + 10.9)/2 = 10.75$

(c) no

48

3.25 (a) $\bar{x}=2(1/10)+3(6/10)+5(2/10)+10(1/10)=40/10=4$

(b) $\bar{x}=2(1000/10000)+3(6000/10000)+5(2000/10000)$
$+10(1000/10000)=4$

3.26 (a) mean $= (13+16+12+9+10)/5 = 60/5 = 12 = 8+4 = \bar{x} + 4$

(b) $\bar{x} + c = 8 + c$

(c) mean $= (18+24+16+10+12)/5 = 80/5 = 16 = 2(8) = 2\bar{x}$

(d) $k\bar{x} = k(8)$

3.27 mean $= 4(\bar{x}) + 7 = 4(6) + 7 = 31$

3.28 (a) $\bar{x} = \sum x/n = 36/6 = 6$ and
$\sum(x-\bar{x}) = (0-6)+(2-6)+(5-6)+(8-6)+(9-6)+(12-6) = 0$

(b) As $\bar{x} = 6$, we would need to supplement the data with
$6 + 2 = 8$ (as $6 - 2 = 4$)

3.29 (a) $\bar{x} = \sum x/n = 94/6 = 15.67$

(b) Ranked data: 1,2,19,22,23,27.
Location median $= (6 + 1)/2 = 3.5$.
Median $= (19 + 22)/2 = 20.5$

(c) no mode

(d) median

3.30 (a) $\bar{x} = \sum x/n = 310/10 = 31$

Ranked data: 12,12,12,13,14,16,17,19,20,175
Location median $= (10+1)/2 = 5.5$, so that
median $= (14 + 16)/2 = 15$

(c) mode $= 12$

(d) median

4.1 (a) 0--This can occur only if the same sum is observed each of the ten times

(b) $12 - 2 = 10$

4.2 (a) $R = 27 - 6 = 21$

(b) $\bar{x} = \sum x/n = 140/10 = 14$

x	x-$\bar{x}$	$(x-\bar{x})^2$
27	13	169
14	0	0
12	-2	4
16	2	4
23	9	81
9	-5	25
7	-7	49
16	2	4
6	-8	64
10	-4	16
Sums: 140		416

$$s^2 = \sum \frac{(x - \bar{x})^2}{n - 1} = \frac{416}{9} = 46.22$$

(c) $s = \sqrt{46.22} = 6.8$

4.3 (a) $R = 36 - 16 = 20$

(b) $\bar{x} = \sum x/n = 156/6 = 26$

x	x-$\bar{x}$	$(x-\bar{x})^2$
24	-2	4
16	-10	100
27	1	1
34	8	64
36	10	100
19	-7	49
Sums: 156		318

$$s^2 = \frac{\sum (x-\bar{x})^2}{n-1} = \frac{318}{5} = 63.6$$

(c) $s = \sqrt{63.6} = 7.97$

4.4   (a)   R = 140 - 116 = 24

      (b)
x	x^2
138	19044
124	15376
116	13456
128	16384
140	19600
136	18496
Sums: 782	102356

$$s^2 = \frac{n(\sum x^2) - (\sum x)^2}{n(n-1)} = \frac{6(102356) - (782)^2}{6(5)} = 87.07$$

      (c) $s = \sqrt{87.07} = 9.33$

4.5   (a)   R = 705 - 473 = 232

      (b) $\bar{x} = \sum x/n = 5700/10 = 570$

x	$x-\bar{x}$	$(x-\bar{x})^2$
623	53	2809
504	-66	4356
519	-51	2601
473	-97	9409
629	59	3481
705	135	18225
513	-57	3249
510	-60	3600
630	60	3600
594	24	576
Sums: 5700		51906

$$s^2 = \frac{\sum(x-\bar{x})^2}{n-1} = \frac{51906}{9} = 5767.33$$

      (c) $s = \sqrt{5767.33} = 75.94$

4.6   (a)   R = 87 - 76 = 11

       (b) $\bar{x} = \sum x/n = 567/7 = 81$

x	x-$\bar{x}$	(x-$\bar{x}$)^2
78	-3	9
83	2	4
86	5	25
77	-4	16
76	-5	25
80	-1	1
87	6	36
Sums: 567		116

$$x = \frac{\sum (x-\bar{x})^2}{n-1} = \frac{116}{6} = 19.33$$

       (c) $s = \sqrt{19.33} = 4.40$

4.7   (a)   R = 33-8 = 25

       (b)

x	x^2
30	900
17	289
18	324
18	324
29	841
32	1024
14	196
10	100
8	64
33	1089
Sums: 209	5151

$$s^2 = \frac{n(\sum x^2) - (\sum x^2)}{n(n-1)}$$

$$= \frac{10(5151) - (209)^2}{(10)(9)} = 86.99$$

       (c) $s = \sqrt{86.99} = 9.33$

4.8 (a) (i)

(ii)

(b) Data set (ii).

(c) (i)

x	x^2
14	196
13	169
12	144
1	1
2	4
3	9
7	49
8	64
Sums: 60	636

$$s^2 = \frac{n(\sum x^2) - (\sum x)^2}{n(n-1)}$$

$$= \frac{8(636) - (60)^2}{(8)(7)} = 26.57$$

$$s = \sqrt{26.57} = 5.15$$

(ii)

x	x^2
20	400
14	196
14	196
14	196
13	169
13	169
13	169
7	49
Sums: 108	1544

$$s^2 = \frac{8(1544) - (108)^2}{(8)(7)} = 12.29$$

$$s = \sqrt{12.29} = 3.51$$

4.9 $\bar{x} = \sum x/n = 30/6 = 5.$

$$s^2 = \frac{\sum (x-\bar{x})^2}{n-1} = \frac{\sum (5-5)^2}{5} = 0$$

4.10 Choose the can of balls with the smaller bounce variability.

4.11 By Chebyshev's theorem, at least $(1 - \frac{1}{2^2})(12) = 9$ scores will lie within two standard deviations of the mean.

$\bar{x} = \sum x/n = 996/12 = 83$

x	x-$\bar{x}$	$(x-\bar{x})^2$
94	11	121
82	-1	1
82	-1	1
77	-6	36
80	-3	9
82	-1	1
87	4	16
86	3	9
80	-3	9
83	0	0
84	1	1
79	-4	16
Sums: 996		220

$$s^2 = \frac{\sum (x - \bar{x})^2}{n - 1} = \frac{220}{11} = 20: \quad s = \sqrt{20} = 4.47$$

$\bar{x} - 2s = 83 - 8.94 = 74.06, \quad \bar{x} + 2s = 83 + 8.94 = 91.94$

Eleven scores lie within two standard deviations of the mean.

4.12 (a) $150 - 2(15) = 120$ and $150 + 2(15) = 180$. So $k = 2$ and $1 - 1/k^2 = 1 - 1/2^2 = 3/4$.

(b) $150 - (6/5)(15) = 132$ and $150 + (6/5)(15) = 168$. So $k = 6/5$ and $1 - 1/k^2 = 1 - 1/(\frac{6}{5})^2 = 11/36$

(c) $150 - 4(15) = 90$ and $150 + 4(15) = 210$. So $k = 4$ and $1 - 1/k^2 = 1 - 1/4^2 = 15/16$

4.13 $$\sigma^2 = \frac{N(\sum x^2) - (\sum x)^2}{N^2}$$

(a)

x	x^2
14	196
14	196
14	196
14	196
0	0
0	0
0	0
0	0
Sums: 56	784

$$\sigma^2 = \frac{8(784) - (56)^2}{8^2} = 49$$

(b)

x	x^2
1	1
2	4
3	9
4	16
5	25
6	36
7	49
Sums: 28	140

$$\sigma^2 = \frac{7(140) - (28)^2}{7^2} = 4$$

(c)

x	x^2
5	25
4	16
4	16
6	36
0	0
1	1
Sums: 20	94

$$\sigma^2 = \frac{6(94) - (20)^2}{36} = 4.56$$

4.14 (a) no   (b) yes

4.15

Class Limits	Frequency f	Class Mark X	Xf	X^2f
0-1	2	0.5	1.0	0.50
2-3	17	2.5	42.5	106.25
4-5	8	4.5	36.0	162.00
6-7	13	6.5	84.5	549.25
8-9	10	8.5	85.0	722.50
Sums:	50 = n		249.0	1540.5

(a) $\bar{x} \doteq \sum Xf/n = 249/50 = 4.98$

(b) $s^2 \doteq \dfrac{n(\sum X^2f) - (\sum Xf)^2}{n(n-1)} = \dfrac{50(1540.5) - (249)^2}{(50)(49)} = 6.13$

$s \doteq \sqrt{6.13} = 2.48$

4.16

Class Limits	Frequency f	Class Mark X	Xf	X^2f
0-2	1	1	1	1
3-5	6	4	24	96
6-8	9	7	63	441
9-11	7	10	70	700
Sums:	23 = n		158	1238

(a) $\bar{x} \doteq \sum Xf/n = 158/23 = 6.87$

(b) $s^2 \doteq \dfrac{n(\sum X^2f) - (\sum Xf)^2}{n(n-1)} = \dfrac{23(1238) - (158)^2}{(23)(22)} = 6.94$

$s \doteq \sqrt{6.94} = 2.63$

4.17

Class Limits	Frequency f	Class Mark X	Xf	X^2f
21-25	6	23	138	3174
26-30	8	28	224	6272
31-35	5	33	165	5445
36-40	7	38	266	10108
41-45	3	43	129	5547
46-50	4	48	192	9216
Sums:	33 = n		1114	39762

(a) $\bar{x} \doteq \sum Xf/n = 1114/33 = 33.76$

(b) $s^2 \doteq \dfrac{n(\sum X^2f) - (\sum Xf)^2}{n(n-1)} = \dfrac{33(39762) - (1114)^2}{(33)(32)} = 67.38$

$s \doteq \sqrt{67.38} = 8.21$

4.18

Class Limits	Frequency f	Class Mark X	Xf	X^2f
33-37	3	35	105	3675
38-42	3	40	120	4800
43-47	8	45	360	16200
48-52	11	50	550	27500
53-57	0	55	0	0
58-62	1	60	60	3600
Sums:	26=n		1195	55775

(a) $\bar{x} \doteq \sum Xf/n = 1195/26 = 45.96$

(b)
$$s^2 \doteq \frac{n(\sum X^2f) - (\sum Xf)^2}{n(n-1)} = \frac{26(55775) - (1195)^2}{(26)(25)} = 34.04$$

$$s \doteq \sqrt{34.04} = 5.83$$

4.19

Class Limits	Frequency f	Class Mark X	Xf	X^2f
210-219	2	214.5	429.0	92020.50
220-229	4	224.5	898.0	201601.00
230-239	9	234.5	2110.5	494912.25
240-249	3	244.5	733.5	179340.75
250-259	1	254.5	254.5	64770.25
260-269	2	264.5	529.0	139920.50
Sums:	21=n		4954.5	1172565.25

(a) $\bar{x} \doteq \sum Xf/n = 4954.5/21 = 235.93$

(b)
$$s^2 \doteq \frac{n(\sum X^2f) - (\sum Xf)^2}{n(n-1)} = \frac{21(1172565.25) - (4954.5)^2}{(21)(20)} = 182.86$$

$$s \doteq \sqrt{182.86} = 13.52$$

4.20 (a) $(m/100)n = (33/100)(30) = 9.9$.
      Location of $P_{33} = 10$, so that $P_{33} = 66$.

      (b) $(m/100)n = (87/100)(30) = 26.1$.
      Location of $P_{87} = 27$, so that $P_{87} = 92$.

      (c) $(m/100)n = (25/100)(30) = 7.5$.
      Location of $Q_1 = 8$, so that $Q_1 = 65$.

      (d) $(m/100)n = (75/100)(30) = 22.5$.
      Location of $Q_3 = 23$, so that $Q_3 = 87$.

      (e) $m = (\dfrac{\text{number of data values less than 74}}{30})(100)$

                                    $= 11(100)/30 = 36.67$.

      (f) $(m/100)n = (30/100)(30) = 9$.
      Location of $D_3 = 9.5$, so that $D_3 = (65+66)/2 = 65.5$

4.21 (a) $(m/100)n = (20/100)(25) = 5$. Location of $P_{20} = 5.5$, so
      that $P_{20} = (0.37 + 0.55)/2 = 0.46$.

      (b) $(m/100)n = (95/100)(25) = 23.75$. Location of $P_{95} = 24$,
      so that $P_{95} = 7.79$.

      (c) $(m/100)n = (50/100)(25) = 12.5$. Location of
      $Q_2 = 13$, so that $Q_2 = 1.15$.

      (d) $m = (\dfrac{\text{number of data values less than 3.69}}{25})(100)$
           $= (19/25)(100) = 76$.

58

4.22 The ranked data are:
```
344   372   392   394   395   405   417   435   440   440
443   444   463   468   469   473   475   479   480   485
492   495   502   503   504   506   515   516   519   525
540   553   555   567   581   582   593   612   620   667
```

(a) $(m/100)n = (15/100)(40) = 6$. Location of $P_{15} = 6.5$, so that $P_{15} = (405 + 417)/2 = 411$.

(b) $(m/100)n = (70/100)(40) = 28$. Location of $P_{70} = 28.5$, so that $P_{70} = (516 + 519)/2 = 517.5$

(c) $(m/100)n = (99/100)(40) = 39.6$. Location of $P_{99} = 40$, so that $P_{99} = 667$.

(d) $m = \left(\dfrac{\text{number of data values less than 525}}{40}\right)(100)$

$= (29/40)(100) = 72.5$

4.23 The ranked data are:
```
1     2     5     5     5     5     5     6     6     6
6     6     6     7     7     8     9     9     9     9
11    11    11    12    12    12    13    14    15    16
16    17    17    17    17    18    19    19    19    19
19    20    21    21    21    22    22    22    22    23
```

(a) $(m/100)n = (20/100)(50) = 10$. Location of $P_{20} = 10.5$, so that $P_{20} = (6 + 6)/2 = 6$.

(b) $(m/100)n = (80/100)(50) = 40$. Location of $P_{80} = 40.5$, so that $P_{80} = (19 + 19)/2 = 19$.

(c) $(m/100)n = (25/100)(50) = 12.5$. Location of $Q_1 = 13$, so that $Q_1 = 6$.

4.24　(a)　$z = \dfrac{x\text{-mean}}{\text{standard deviation}}$

       (i)　$z = (30 - 30)/10 = 0$

      (ii)　$z = (50 - 30)/10 = 2$

     (iii)　$z = (10 - 30)/10 = -2$

      (iv)　$z = (65 - 30)/10 = 3.5$

(b)　$x = z(\text{standard deviation}) + \text{mean}$

       (i)　$x = (10)(-2) + 30 = 10$

      (ii)　$x = (10)(1) + 30 = 40$

     (iii)　$x = (10)(2.5) + 30 = 55$

      (iv)　$x = (10)(1.5) + 30 = 45$

       (v)　$x = (10)(0) + 30 = 30$

4.25　(a)　$z = \dfrac{x\text{-mean}}{\text{standard deviation}}$

       (i)　$z = (30 - 40)/15 = -0.67$

      (ii)　$z = (50 - 40)/15 = 0.67$

     (iii)　$z = (10 - 40)/15 = -2$

      (iv)　$z = (65 - 40)/15 = 1.67$

(b)　$x = z(\text{standard deviation}) + \text{mean}$

       (i)　$x = (15)(-2) + 40 = 10$

      (ii)　$x = (15)(1) + 40 = 55$

     (iii)　$x = (15)(2.5) + 40 = 77.5$

      (iv)　$x = (15)(1.5) + 40 = 62.5$

       (v)　$x = (15)(0) + 40 = 40$

4.26 $$z = \frac{x - \text{mean}}{\text{standard deviation}}$$

mathematics: $z = (70 - 65)/5 = 1$.

economics: $z = (79 - 74)/10 = 0.5$.

Your mathematics score was better relative to the class.

4.27 $$z = \frac{x - \text{mean}}{\text{standard deviation}} \qquad x = (\text{standard deviation}) + \text{mean}$$

biology: $z = (80 - 60)/15 = 1.33$ $\qquad$ statistics: $z = 1.5$

(a) statistics $\qquad$ (b) $x = (1.5)(6) + 78 = 87$

4.28 95

4.29 (a) $R = 34 - 14 = 20$

(b) $\bar{x} = \sum x/n = 140/7 = 20$

x	$x - \bar{x}$	$(x - \bar{x})^2$
19	-1	1
17	-3	9
14	-6	36
21	1	1
19	-1	1
16	-4	16
34	14	196
Sum: 140		260

$$s^2 = \frac{\sum (x - \bar{x})^2}{n-1} = \frac{260}{6} = 43.33$$

(c) $s = \sqrt{43.33} = 6.58$

(d) Ranked data: 14, 16, 17, 19, 19, 21, 34
$(m/100)n = (25/100)7 = 1.75$. Location of $Q_1 = 2$, so that $Q_1 = 16$.

(e) $(m/100)n = (60/100)7 = 4.2$. Location of $P_{60} = 5$, so that $P_{60} = 19$.

4.30   (a)   R = 211 - 60 = 151

(b)

x	x^2
118	13924
173	29929
110	12100
149	22201
93	8649
211	44521
172	29584
161	25921
145	21025
143	20449
60	3600
112	12544
206	42436
165	27225
81	6561
168	28224
130	16900
Sums: 2397	365793

$$s^2 = \frac{n\left(\sum x^2\right) - \left(\sum x\right)^2}{n(n-1)}$$

$$= \frac{17(365793) - (2397)^2}{(17)(16)} = 1738.5$$

(c) $s = \sqrt{1738.5} = 41.70$

(d)   Ranked data: 60, 81, 93, 110, 112, 118, 130, 143, 145, 149, 161, 165, 168, 172, 173, 206, 211

$(m/100)n = (25/100)(17) = 4.25$. Location of $Q_1 = 5$, so that $Q_1 = 112$.

(e) $(m/100)n = (60/100)(17) = 10.2$. Location of $P_{60} = 11$, so that $P_{60} = 161$.

4.31   (a)   R = 175 - 12 = 163

    (b)

x	x^2
12	144
14	196
12	144
16	256
17	289
19	361
12	144
13	169
20	400
175	30625
Sums: 310	32728

$$s^2 = \frac{n\left(\sum x^2\right) - \left(\sum x\right)^2}{n(n-1)}$$

$$= \frac{10(32728) - (310)^2}{(10)(9)} = 2568.67$$

    (c) $s = \sqrt{2568.67} = 50.68$

    (d)   Ranked data: 12, 12, 12, 13, 14, 16, 17, 19, 20, 175
          $(m/100)n = (25/100)(10) = 2.5$. Location of $Q_1 = 3$,
          so that $Q_1 = 12$.

    (e) $(m/100)n = (60/100)(10) = 6$. Location of $P_{60} = 6.5$,
          so that $P_{60} = (16 + 17)/2 = 16.5$.

4.32

Class Limits	Frequency f	Class Mark X	Xf	X^2f
9-17	14	13	182	2366
18-26	9	22	198	4356
27-35	7	31	217	6727
36-44	4	40	160	6400
45-53	3	49	147	7203
54-62	1	58	58	3364
Sums:	38		962	30416

$$s \doteq \sqrt{\frac{n\left(\sum X^2 f\right) - \left(\sum Xf\right)^2}{n(n-1)}} = \sqrt{\frac{(38)(30416) - (962)^2}{(38)(37)}} = 12.8$$

4.33

Class Limits	Frequency f	Class Mark X	Xf	X^2f
9-17	1	13	13	169
18-26	3	22	66	1452
27-35	4	31	124	3844
36-44	7	40	280	11200
45-53	9	49	441	21609
54-62	14	58	812	47096
Sums:	38		1736	85370

$$s \doteq \sqrt{\frac{n(\sum X^2 f) - (\sum Xf)^2}{n(n-1)}} = \sqrt{\frac{(38)(85370) - (1736)^2}{(38)(37)}} = 12.8$$

4.34 (a) $R = 32 - 10 = 22$

(b)

x	x^2
23	529
14	196
10	100
10	100
32	1024
31	961
20	400
Sums: 140	3310

$$s^2 = \frac{n(\sum x^2) - (\sum x)^2}{n(n-1)}$$

$$= \frac{7(3310) - (140)^2}{(7)(6)} = 85$$

(c) $s = \sqrt{85} = 9.22$

(d) $\bar{x} = \sum x/n = 140/7 = 20.$

$$z = \frac{x - mean}{standard\ deviation} = (14 - 20)/9.22 = -0.65.$$

4.35 $x = z$(standard deviation) + mean

   (a) $x = (-2.5)(25) + 400 = 337.5$

   (b) $x = 1(25) + 400 = 425$

   (c) $x = (3.2)(25) + 400 = 480$

   (d) $x = 0(25) + 400 = 400$

   (e) $400 - 4(25) = 300$ and $400 + 4(25) = 500$.   So $k = 4$
         and $(1 - 1/4^2)(1000) = 937.5$.   At least 937 data values
         lie between 300 and 500.

   (f) $400 - 2(25) = 350$ and $400 + 2(25) = 450$.   So $k = 2$
         and $(1 - 1/2^2)(1000) = 750$.   At least 750 data values
         lie between 350 and 450.   At most 250 data values are
         smaller than 350 or larger than 450.

4.36   Albany: $R = 71.4 - 21.1 = 50.3$
       Reno: $R = 69.5 - 32.2 = 37.3$

4.37   Albany:

x	x^2		Reno:	x	x^2
21.1	445.21			32.2	1036.84
23.4	547.56			37.4	1398.76
33.6	1128.96			40.6	1648.36
46.6	2171.56			46.4	2152.96
57.5	3306.25			54.6	2981.16
66.7	4448.89			62.4	3893.76
71.4	5097.96			69.5	4830.25
69.2	4788.64			66.9	4475.61
61.2	3745.44			60.2	3624.04
50.5	2550.25			50.3	2530.09
39.3	1544.49			39.7	1576.09
26.5	702.25			32.5	1056.25
Sums: 567.0	30477.46		Sums:	592.7	31204.17

$\bar{x} = \sum x/n = 567/12 = 47.25$ $\bar{x} = 592.7/12 = 49.39$

4.38   Albany:
$$s^2 = \frac{n(\sum x^2) - (\sum x)^2}{n(n-1)}$$

$$= \frac{(12)(30477.46) - (567)^2}{(12)(11)} = 335.16$$

$$s = \sqrt{335.16} = 18.31$$

Reno:
$$s^2 = \frac{(12)(31204.17) - (592.7)^2}{(12)(11)} = 175.43$$

$$s = \sqrt{175.43} = 13.24$$

4.39   Albany:

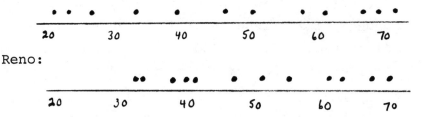

Reno:

4.40   The mean temperatures are the same, but the temperatures in Reno are less variable.

4.41   Ranked data: 35, 48, 54, 60, 71, 107, 123, 150, 212

x	x^2
35	1225
48	2304
54	2916
60	3600
71	5041
107	11449
123	15129
150	22500
212	44944
Sums: 860	109108

(a) $\bar{x} = \sum x/n = 860/9 = 95.56$

(b) $s^2 = \frac{n(\sum x^2) - (\sum x)^2}{n(n-1)} = \frac{9(109108) - (860)^2}{9(8)} = 3366.28$

$s = \sqrt{3366.28} = 58.02$

(c) Location of median = $(9 + 1)/2 = 5$, so that median = 71.

4.42   Ranked data: 35, 48, 54, 60, 71, 107, 123, 150

x	x^2
35	1225
48	2304
54	2916
60	3600
71	5041
107	11449
123	15129
150	22500
Sums: 648	64164

(a) $\bar{x} = \sum x/n = 648/8 = 81$

(b)
$$s^2 = \frac{n(\sum x^2) - (\sum x)^2}{n(n - 1)} = \frac{8(64164) - (648)^2}{8(7)} = 1668$$

$s = \sqrt{1668} = 40.84$

(c)   Location of median $= (8 + 1)/2 = 4.5$, so that
median $= (60 + 71)/2 = 65.5$

The mean and standard deviation have changed the most.

4.43   (a) $\bar{x} = \sum x/n = 497.5/33 = 15.076$

(b)
$$s^2 = \frac{n(\sum x^2) - (\sum x)^2}{n(n - 1)} = 77.286$$

$$= \frac{(33)(9973.33) - (497.5)^2}{(33)(32)}$$

$s = \sqrt{77.286} = 8.791$

(c)   Location of median $= (33 + 1)/2 = 17$, so that
median $= 13.8$.

(d) $(m/100)n = (95/100)(33) = 31.35$.   Location of $P_{95} = 32$,
so that $P_{95} = 32.4$.

(e) $(m/100)n = (10/100)(33) = 3.3$.   Location of $P_{10} = 4$,
so that $P_{10} = 4.5$.

4.43   (f) $1 - 1/k^2 = 1 - 1/2^2 = 3/4$ and $(3/4)(33) = 24.75$.
So at least 24 data values will lie within
2 standard deviations of the mean.

Now $\bar{x} - 2s \doteq 15.076 - 2(8.791) = -2.506$
and $\bar{x} + 2s \doteq 15.076 + 2(8.791) = 32.658$

So 32 data values lie within 2 standard deviations
of the mean.

4.44   (a) $z = (x - \bar{x})/s = (32.8 - 15.076)/8.791 = 2.02$

(b) $z = (x - \bar{x})/s = (2.3 - 15.076)/8.791 = -1.45$

4.45   (a) $x = zs + \bar{x} = (-.862)(8.791) + 15.076 = 7.5$

Detroit

(b) $x = (1.027)(8.791) + 15.076 = 24.1$

El Paso

4.46   (a) $(m/100)n = (12/100)(33) = 3.96$.   The city is Buffalo.

(b) $(m/100)n = (91/100)(33) = 30.03$.   The city is Portland.

4.47   (a) $\mu = \sum x/N = 3487/50 = 69.74$

(b)
$$\sigma^2 = \frac{N(\sum x^2) - (\sum x)^2}{N^2} = \frac{(50)(495181) - (3487)^2}{(50)^2} = 5039.95$$

So $\sigma = \sqrt{5039.95} = 70.99$

(c)   Location of median $= (50 + 1)/2 = 25.5$, so that
median $= (49 + 49)/2 = 49$.

(d) $(m/100)n = (90/100)(50) = 45$.   Location of $P_{90} = 45.5$,
so that $P_{90} = (166 + 184)/2 = 175$.

(e) $(m/100)n = (25/100)(50) = 12.5$.   Location of $Q_1 = 13$,
so that $Q_1 = 17$.

(f) $(m/100)n = (75/100)(50) = 37.5$.   Location of $Q_3 = 38$,
so that $Q_3 = 83$.

4.48   (a) $(1 - 1/k^2)(50) = (1 - 1/2^2)(50) = 37.5$. At least 37 data values lie within 2 standard deviations of the mean. $(1 - 1/k^2)(50) = (1 - 1/3^2)(50) = 44.44$. At least 44 data values lie within 3 standard deviations of the mean.

      (b) $\mu - 2\sigma = 69.74 - 2(70.99) = -72.24$.

          $\mu + 2\sigma = 69.74 + 2(70.99) = 211.72$.

There are 48 data values within 2 standard deviations of the mean.

          $\mu - 3\sigma = 69.74 - 3(70.99) = -143.23$

          $\mu + 3\sigma = 69.74 + 3(70.99) = 282.71$

There are 48 data values within 3 standard deviations of the mean.

4.49

Class Limits	Frequency f	Class Mark X	Xf	X^2f
1- 25	15	13	195	2535
26- 50	12	38	456	17328
51- 75	8	63	504	31752
76-100	6	88	528	46464
101-125	1	113	113	12769
126-150	1	138	138	19044
151-175	2	163	326	53138
176-200	1	188	188	35344
201-225	2	213	426	90738
226-250	0	238	0	0
251-275	0	263	0	0
276-300	1	288	288	82944
301-325	1	313	313	97969
Sums:	50		3475	490025

(a) $\mu \doteq \sum Xf/N = 3475/50 = 69.5$

(b)

$$\sigma \doteq \sqrt{\frac{N(\sum X^2 f) - (\sum Xf)^2}{N^2}} = \sqrt{\frac{(50)(490025) - (3475)^2}{2500}}$$

$$= 70.5$$

4.50 (a) $\bar{x} = \sum x/n = \dfrac{105576}{35} = 3016.46$

(b) $s = \sqrt{\dfrac{n(\sum x^2) - (\sum x)^2}{n(n-1)}} = \sqrt{\dfrac{(35)(2192885750) - (105576)^2}{(35)(34)}}$

$= 7424.96$

(c) Location of median $= (35+1)/2 = 18$, so that median $= 242$.

(a) $(m/100)(35) = (80/100)(35) = 28$. Location of $P_{80} = 28.5$, so that $P_{80} = (1000 + 1679)/2 = 1339.5$.

(e) $(m/100)(35) = (25/100)(35) = 8.75$. Location of $Q_1 = 9$, so that $Q_1 = 142$.

(f) $(m/100)(35) = (75/100)(35) = 26.25$. Location of $Q_3 = 27$, so that $Q_3 = 700$.

4.51

Class Limits	Frequency f	Class Mark X	Xf	X²f
100- 3260	30	1680	50400	84672000
3261- 6421	0	4841	0	0
6422- 9582	1	8002	8002	64032004
9583-12743	1	11163	11163	124612569
12744-15904	0	14324	0	0
15905-19065	0	17485	0	0
19066-22226	0	20646	0	0
22227-25387	2	23807	47614	1133546498
25388-28548	0	26968	0	0
28549-31709	1	30129	30129	907756641
Sums:	35		147308	2314619712

(a) $\bar{x} \doteq \sum Xf/N = 147308/35 = 4208.8$

(b) $s \doteq \sqrt{\dfrac{n(\sum X^2 f) - (\sum Xf)^2}{n(n-1)}} = \sqrt{\dfrac{(35)(2314619712) - (147308)^2}{(35)(34)}}$

$= 7059.89$

4.51   (c)

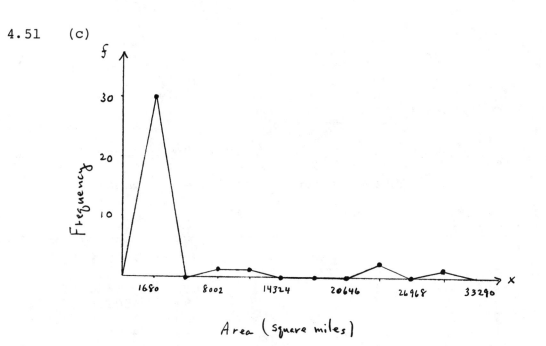

Area (square miles)

skewed to the right

(d)

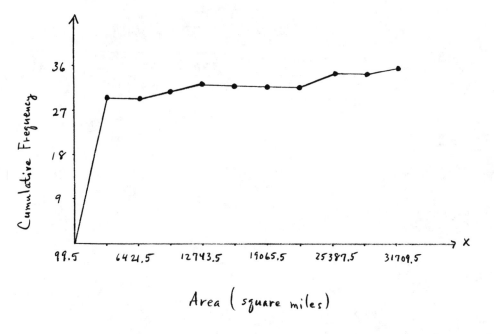

Area (square miles)

4.52 (a) mean

(b) $\bar{x} = \sum x/n = 11316/30 = 377.2.$ Location of median $= (30+1)/2$
= 15.5, so that median = $(197 + 207)/2 = 202.$
The mean has decreased considerably, whereas the
median has remained quite stable.

(c)
$$s = \sqrt{\frac{n(\sum x^2) - (\sum x)^2}{n(n-1)}} = \sqrt{\frac{(30)(9161950) - (11316)^2}{(30)(29)}}$$
$= 410.78$
The standard deviation has decreased considerably.

4.53

Class Limits	Frequency f	Class Mark X	Xf	X^2f
95- 227	17	161	2737	440657
228- 360	3	294	882	259308
361- 493	5	427	2135	911645
494- 626	1	560	560	313600
627- 759	1	693	693	480249
760- 892	0	826	0	0
893-1025	1	959	959	919681
1026-1158	0	1092	0	0
1159-1291	0	1225	0	0
1292-1424	0	1358	0	0
1425-1557	0	1491	0	0
1558-1690	2	1624	3248	5274752
Sums:	30		11214	8599892

(a) $\bar{x} \doteq \sum Xf/n = 11214/30 = 373.8$

(b)
$$s \doteq \sqrt{\frac{n(\sum X^2 f) - (\sum Xf)^2}{n(n-1)}} = \sqrt{\frac{(30)(8599892) - (11214)^2}{(30)(29)}} = 389.88$$

4.53   (c)

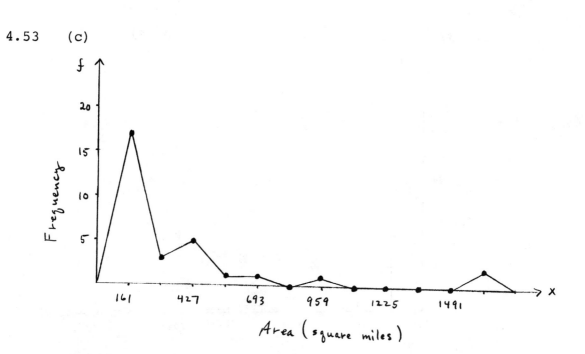

skewed to the right

(d)

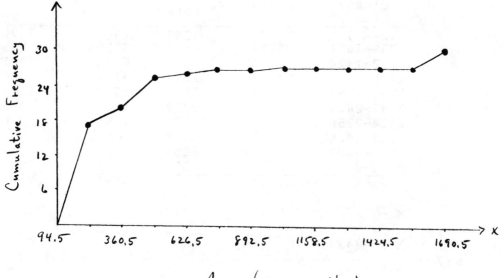

4.54   (a)   37   47   52   54   57   59   60   60   60   61

(b)

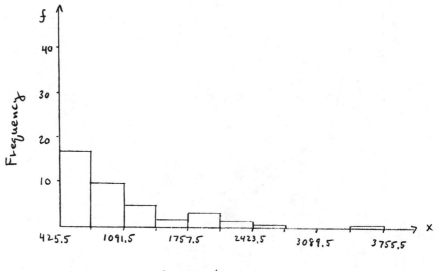

Length (miles)

(c)   first

(d)

Class Limits	Frequency f	Class Mark X	Xf	X²f
426- 758	37	592	21904	12967168
759-1091	10	925	9250	8556250
1092-1424	5	1258	6290	7912820
1425-1757	2	1591	3182	5062562
1758-2090	3	1924	5772	11105328
2091-2423	2	2257	4514	10188098
2424-2756	1	2590	2590	6708100
2757-3089	0	2923	0	0
3090-3422	0	3256	0	0
3423-3755	1	3589	3589	12880921
Sums:	61		57091	75381247

$$\bar{x} \doteq \sum Xf/n = 57091/61 = 935.92$$

(e) $$s \doteq \sqrt{\frac{n(\sum X^2 f) - (\sum Xf)^2}{n(n-1)}} = \sqrt{\frac{(61)(75381247) - (57091)^2}{(61)(60)}} = 604.82$$

4.55　(a)

x	x^2
3	9
5	25
8	64
11	121
12	144
15	225
Sums: 54	588

$$s^2 = \frac{n\left(\sum x^2\right) - \left(\sum x\right)^2}{n(n-1)}$$

$$= \frac{6(588) - (54)^2}{(6)(5)} = 20.4$$

(b)　$s^2 = 20.4$

(c)

x	x^2
0	0
4	16
10	100
16	256
18	324
24	576
Sums: 72	1272

$$s^2 = \frac{6(1272) - (72)^2}{(6)(5)} = 81.6$$

$$= (2)^2(20.4)$$

(d)　$s^2 k^2$

4.56　new variance $= (4)^2(3.5) = 56$

75

5.1 (a) S = {O,A,B,AB}.

(b) S={OO,OA,OB,O<u>AB</u>,AO,AA,AB,A<u>AB</u>,BO,BA,BB,B<u>AB</u>,<u>AB</u>O,<u>AB</u>A,
<u>AB</u>B,<u>ABAB</u>}.

5.2 S = {xX,xY,XX,XY}.

5.3 S = {xX,XY}.

5.4 S = {HHH,HHT,HTH,THH,TTH,THT,HTT,TTT}.

(a) E = {HHH}.

(b) E = {HHH,HHT,THH,THT}.

(c) E = {TTH,THT,HTT}.

5.5 (a) E={4260,4261,4262,4263,4264,4265,4266,4267,4268,4269}.

(b) E = {2468,2648,4268,4628,6248,6428}.

5.6 (a) E = {SS}.

(b) E = {SS,CC}.

(c) E = {CH,HC,DH,HD,SH,HS,HH}.

(d) E = {CD,HD,DD,SD}.

5.7 S = {0A,0B,0C,0D,0E,1A,1B,1C,1D,1E}.

(a) E = {0D,0E}.   (b) E = {1A,1B,1C,1D}.

(c) E = {0A,0B,1A,1B}.   (d) E = {1A,1B,1C,1D,1E}.

5.8 (a) E = {M1,M2,M3,F1,F2,F3}.

(b) E = {F1,F2,F3,F4,F5,F6,M4,M5,M6}.

(c) E = {M6}.

(d) E = {M3}.

5.9 (a) S = {M,F}.

(b) P(female) = 20/34 = 0.5882.

5.10 (a) P(sum of two dice is less than 5) = 6/36 = 0.1667.

(b) P(at least one 6) = 11/36 = 0.3056.

(c) P(sum is either 7 or 11) = 8/36 = 0.2222.

5.11 (a) P(ace) = 4/52 = 0.0769.

(b) P(not a 9) = 48/52 = 0.9231.

5.12 (a) S = {0,1,2,3,4,5,6,7,8,9}.

(b) A = {1,3,5,7,9}. P(A) = 5/10 = 0.5.

(c) A = {7,8,9}. P(A) = 3/10 = 0.3.

5.13   (a)   P(two boys) = 6/16 = 0.375

       (b)   P(all girls) = 1/16 = 0.0625

       (c)   P(oldest two are boys) = 4/16 = 0.25

5.14   (a)   S = {EEEE,EEEO,EEOE,EOEE,OEEE,EEOO,EOOE,OOEE,EOEO,
                  OEOE,OEEO,OOOE,OOEO,OEOO,EOOO,OOOO}.

       (b)   P(all evens) = 1/16 = 0.0625.

       (c)   P(at least one even) = 15/16 = 0.9375.

       (d)   P(at least two evens in succession) = 8/16 = 0.5.

5.15   (a)   P(received a master's degree)

             $$= \frac{75 + 209 + 298}{395 + 833 + 999 + 75 + 209 + 298} = \frac{582}{2809} = 0.2072.$$

       (b)   P(received a degree in 1970) = (833 + 209)/2809 = 0.371

5.16   (a)   B,C

       (b)   (i)   P(A or B) = (15/36) + (18/36) - (9/36) = 0.6667

              (ii)   P(B or C) = (18/36) + (18/36) = 1

             (iii)   P(A or D) = (15/36) + (33/36) - (12/36) = 1

       (c)   P(A or E or F) = (15/36) + (3/36) + (1/36) = 0.5278

5.17   (a)   A,B

       (b)   (i)   P(A or B) = (4/52) + (12/52) = 0.3077

              (ii)   P(A or C) = (4/52) + (13/52) - (1/52) = 0.3077

             (iii)   P(B or C) = (12/52) + (13/52) - (3/52) = 0.4231

5.18   P(male or under the age of 25) = (1500/4000)+(3600/4000)
          - (1200/4000) = 0.975.

5.19   S = {xX,xY,XX,XY}.

       (a)   1/4 to each outcome.

       (b)   P(carry color-blind gene or be color-blind)=2/4 = 0.5.

5.20   (a)   P(A) = (100 + 1000)/2000 = 0.55

       (b)   P($\overline{B}$) = (1000 + 200)/2000 = 0.6

       (c)   P(A and B) = 100/2000 = 0.05

       (d)   P(A or B) = (1100/2000) + (800/2000) - (100/2000) = 0.9

       (e)   P(A or $\overline{B}$) = (1100/2000)+(1200/2000)-(1000/2000) = 0.65

5.21   (a)   (i)   P(A and B) = (4/52)(3/51) = 0.0045

              (ii)   P(B) = (4/52)(3/51) + (48/52)(4/51) = 0.0769

             (iii)   P(A or B)=(4/52)+(4/52)-(4/52)(3/51) = 0.1493

5.21   (b)   No. $P(B|A) = 3/51 = 0.0588$ and $P(A) = 4/52 = 0.0769$.

5.22   (a)   (i) $P(A \text{ and } B) = (4/52)(4/52) = 0.0059$.

           (ii) $P(B) = 4/52 = 0.0769$.

           (iii) $P(A \text{ or } B) = (4/52) + (4/52) - (4/52)(4/52)$
                   $= 0.1479$.   A and B are independent.

       (b) $P(A \text{ and } B \text{ and } C) = (4/52)(4/52)(48/52) = 0.0055$.

5.23   (a)   (i) $P(A|C) = 14/26 = 0.5385$.

           (ii) $P(C|A) = 14/18 = 0.7778$.

           (iii) $P(B|C) = 4/26 = 0.1538$.

       (b)   (i)   1   (ii)   0

       (c)   None of the pairs of events is independent.

5.24 $P(\text{both are males}) = (2/7)(1/6) = 0.0476$.

5.25   (a) $P(\text{color-blind}|\text{a male}) = 0.25/0.5 = 0.5$.

       (b) $P(\text{color-blind}|\text{a female}) = 0/0.5 = 0$.

5.26   (a) $P(\text{satisfied}) = 9/10 = 0.9$.

       (b)   (i) $P(\text{both cans are satisfactory}) = (9/10)(9/10)$
                        $= 0.81$.

           (ii) $P(\text{exactly one can is satisfactory})$
                   $= (9/10)(1/10) + (1/10)(9/10) = 0.18$.

           (iii) $P(\text{at least one can is satisfactory})$
                    $= 0.81 + 0.18 = 0.99$.

5.27 $P(\text{male}|\text{employed more than 20 years}) = 30/70 = 0.4286$.

5.28 $P(\text{commit a crime}|\text{employed}) = (0.05)(0.1)/0.7 = 0.0071$.

5.29   (a) $P(\text{female}|\text{no opinion}) = 10/(6 + 10) = 0.625$.

       (b) $P(\text{approves of change}|\text{male}) = 21/(21+6+12) = 0.5385$.

       (c) $P(\text{male}|\text{does not approve of change}) = 12/(12+7) = 0.6316$.

       (d) $P(\text{male and approves of change})$
             $= (\dfrac{21}{21+14})(\dfrac{21 + 14}{21 + 14 + 6 + 10 + 12 + 7}) = 0.3$.

5.30   (a) $P(\text{husband earns less than } \$20000|\text{wife earns less than}$
             $\$20000) = 430/(430 + 410) = 0.5119$.

       (b) $P(\text{wife earns more than } \$20000|\text{husband earns more}$
             $\text{than } \$20000) = 100/(410 + 100) = 0.1961$.

       (c)   No. $P(\text{husband} < \$20000) = \dfrac{430 + 60}{1000} = 0.49$
             $\neq P(\text{husband} < \$20000|\text{wife} < \$20000) = 0.5119$

5.31 P(cancer|test indicates cancer)

$$= \frac{(0.02)(0.99)}{(0.02)(0.99) + (0.005)(0.98)} = \frac{(0.02)(0.99)}{0.0247} = 0.8016$$

5.32 (a) P((A and B)|A) = 0.25/0.5 = 0.5.

(b) P((A and B)|(A or B)) = 1/3 = 0.3333.

5.33 P(at least one 6) = 1−P(no 6's) = 1 − $(5/6)^3$ = 0.4213.

5.34 P(at least one woman) = 1 − P(no women)
= 1 − (8/10)(7/9) = 0.3778.

5.35 P(at least one child has disease)
= 1−P(no child has disease)=1−$(9/10)^4$ = 0.3439.

5.36 P(at least one defective item) = 1 − P(no defective items)
= 1 − $(0.98)^5$ = 0.0961.

5.37 P(at least two principals select same grade level)
= 1 − P(no two principals select same grade level)
= 1 − (7/8)(6/8)(5/8) = 0.5898.

5.38 S = {R1,R2,R3,R4,B1,B2,B3,B4,G1,G2,G3,G4}

5.39 S={11,12,13,14,21,22,23,24,31,32,33,34,41,42,43,44}

5.40 (a) {cc}

(b) {Cc,cC}

5.41 (a) {1ax,2ax,3ax,4ax,5ax,1bx,2bx,3bx,4bx,5bx}

(b) {1ax,1ay,3ax,3ay}

(c) {1bx,2bx,3bx,4bx,5bx}

5.42 (a) S = {WW,WL,LW,LL}   (b) (i) {WW}   (ii) {WL,LW}

5.43 (a) S = {eee,eeo,eoe,oee,ooe,oeo,eoo,ooo}

(b) (i) {ooe,oeo,eoo}   (ii) {ooo}

5.44 (a) P(Democrat) = 417/(417 + 335 + 248) = 0.417

(b) P(Democrat or Independent)= (417 + 248)/1000 = 0.665

(c) P(no Independent) = 1 − 248/1000 = 0.752

5.45 (a) P(your birthdate) = 1/365 = 0.0027

(b) P(a day in July) = 31/365 = 0.0849

(c) P(first day of any month) = 12/365 = 0.0329

(d) P(month begins with J) = (31 + 30 + 31)/365 = 0.2521

5.46   The population size is 9350.

        (a)   P(New England) = 154/9350 = 0.0165.

        (b)   P(one of the Central states)
               = (1665 + 481 + 640 + 1454)/9350 = 0.4535.

5.47   (a)   S = {2H,2T,3H,3T,4H,4T,5H,5T,6H,6T,7H,7T,8H,8T,9H,
                    9T,10,11,12}.

        (b)   (i)   P(head) =
                      (1/36)(1/2)+(2/36)(1/2)+(3/36)(1/2)+(4/36)(1/2)
                      +(5/36)(1/2)+(6/36)(1/2)+(5/36)(1/2)+(4/36)(1/2)
                      = 0.4167.

               (ii)   P(head or tail) = 1 - P(10 or 11 or 12)
                      = 1 - (3/36+2/36+1/36) = 0.8333.

        (c)   P(sum of 8 and a tail) = (5/36)(1/2) = 0.0694.

5.48   (a)   P(both are defective) = (3/10)(2/9) = 0.0667.

        (b)   P(at least 1 defective) = 1 - P(no defectives)
               = 1 - (7/10)(6/9) = 0.5333.

        (c)   P(1 defective) = (3/10)(7/9) + (7/10)(3/9) = 0.4667.

5.49   (a)   P(oldest child is color-blind and other child is
               not color-blind) = (1/4)(3/4) = 0.1875.

        (b)   P(one child is color-blind) = (1/4)(3/4)+(3/4)(1/4)
               = 0.375.

        (c)   P(both children are color-blind) = $(1/4)^2$ = 0.0625.

        (d)   P(at least one child is color-blind)
               = 1-P(neither child is color-blind)=1-$(3/4)^2$=0.4375.

5.50   (a)   P(none approves) = $(.3)^4$ = 0.0081.

        (b)   P(exactly two approve) = $6(.7)^2(.3)^2$ = 0.2646.

        (c)   P(at least one approves) = 1 - P(none approves)
               = 1 - $(.3)^4$ = 0.9919.

5.51   (a)   P(S wins in four games) = $(3/5)^4$ = 0.1296.

        (b)   P(series lasts exactly five games)

               = $4(3/5)^4(2/5) + 4(2/5)^4(3/5)$ = 0.2688.

5.52   (a)   P(both cars fail to start) = (2/10)(3/10) = 0.06.

        (b)   P(at least one fails to start)=1-P(both start)
               = 1 - (8/10)(7/10) = 0.44.

        (c)   P(exactly one fails to start)
               = (2/10)(7/10) + (8/10)(3/10) = 0.38.

5.53　(a)　P(both arrive at 1:30) = $(1/3)^2$ = 0.1111.

(b)　P(both arrive at same time) = $3(1/3)^2$ = 0.3333.

(c)　P(S arrives 30 minutes before T) = $2(1/3)^2$ = 0.2222.

5.54　(a)　P(husband does not live for 25 more years)
= 1 - (7/10) = 0.3.

(b)　P(both live for 25 more years) = (7/10)(9/10) = 0.63.

(c)　P(at least one lives for 25 more years)
= 1 - P(both live less than 25 more years)
= 1 - (3/10)(1/10) = 0.97.

5.55　P(your number is selected) = $(1/10)^4$ = 0.0001

5.56　P(malignant|thyroid tumor) = 0.06/0.31 = 0.1935.

5.57　(a)　(400 + 75 + 15 + 5)/1000 = 0.495.

(b)　(190 + 35 + 75 + 15 + 10 + 5)/1000 = 0.33.

(c)　(400 + 190 + 75 + 15 + 10 + 5)/1000 = 0.695.

5.58　(a)　P(not enrolled in English I)
= 1 - P(enrolled in English I) = 1 - 0.9 = 0.1.

(b)　P(enrolled in English I or Mathematics I)
= 0.8 + 0.9 - 0.75 = 0.95.

(c)　P(enrolled in English I|enrolled in Mathematics I)
= 0.75/0.80 = 0.9375.

5.59　(a)　(40 + 20)/150 = 0.4.

(b)　(40 + 40 + 5)/150 = 0.5667.

(c)　40/(40 + 10) = 0.8.

(d)　40/85 = 0.4706.

(e)　$\dfrac{(40 + 20) + (40 + 40 + 5) - 40}{150}$ = 0.7

(f)　The events are not mutually exclusive, because some
businessmen approve.　The events are not independent.
Note that (proportion of businessmen)
(proportion of approve) = (60/150)(85/150) = 0.2267
while (proportion of businessmen and approve)
= 40/150 = 0.2667.

5.60 (a) Let R1,R2,G1,G2,G3,G4 represent the balls in urn I, and R3,R4,R5,G5,G6,G7,G8,G9 represent the balls in urn II. The sample space S consists of all ordered pairs. For example, (R2,G8) is an element of S.

(b) P(both green) = (4/6)(5/8) = 0.4167.

(c) P(at least one green) = 1 - P(neither is green)
= 1 - (2/6)(3/8) = 0.875.

5.61 (a) S = {(I,R),(II,R),(I,G),(II,G)}.

(b) P(green) = (1/2)(4/6) + (1/2)(5/8) = $\frac{31}{48}$ = 0.6458.

(c) P(urnI | green) = $\frac{(1/2)(4/6)}{(31/48)}$ = 0.5161.

5.62 P(green) = (4/6)(6/9) + (2/6)(5/9) = 0.6296.

Chapter 6

6.1   (a)   discrete   (b)   continuous   (c)   continuous
             (d)   discrete   (e)   continuous

6.2   (a)   2,3,4,...,12.   discrete

        (b) $0, \pm1, \pm2, \pm3, \pm4, \pm5$

6.3   (a)   0,1,2,3,4.   discrete   (b)   0,1,2,3,4,5.

6.4   (a)   0,1,2,3,...,100.   (b)   discrete

6.5   (a) $x \geq 0$ (b)   continuous

6.6   (a)   breaking strength   (b)   continuous

6.7

x	P(x)
5000	1/15
5700	2/15
6600	1/15
7200	1/15
7300	4/15
7800	2/15
8400	2/15
9000	2/15

6.8

x	P(x)
0	1/5
1	1/5
2	3/5

6.9

x	P(x)
1	7326/12079
2	1748/12079
3	794/12079
4	840/12079
5	1371/12079

6.10

x	P(x)
2	1/36
3	2/36
4	3/36
5	4/36
6	5/36
7	6/36
8	5/36
9	4/36
10	3/36
11	2/36
12	1/36

6.11

x	P(x)
70	1/25
72	1/25
73	2/25
74	4/25
75	4/25
76	3/25
77	2/25
78	3/25
79	3/25
80	2/25

6.12

x	P(x)
0	5/30
1	4/30
2	3/30
3	5/30
4	9/30
5	4/30

6.13   No: $\sum P(x) \neq 1$.

6.14   No; P(x) cannot be negative.   P(x) cannot be larger than 1.
$\sum P(x) \neq 1$.

6.15   Yes.

6.16   Yes.

6.17

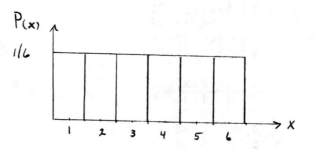

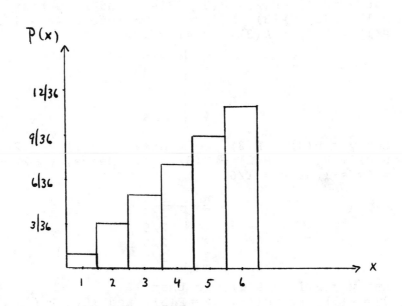

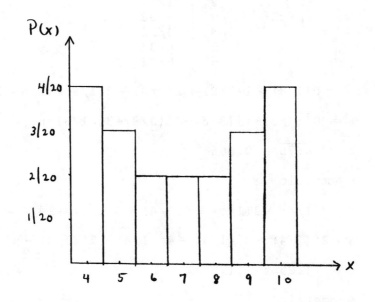

6.20   Let $y = P(1) = P(2) = P(3) = P(4)$, and note that
        $P(1) + P(2) + P(3) + P(4) = 1$. Therefore $4y = 1$ or
        $P(1) = P(2) = P(3) = P(4) = 1/4$.

x	P(x)
1	1/4
2	1/4
3	1/4
4	1/4

6.21   Let $y = P(0) = P(3)$, so that $2y = P(1) = P(2)$. But
        $P(0) + P(1) + P(2) + P(3) = 1$. Hence, $y + 2y + 2y + y$
        $= 6y = 1$ or $y = 1/6$.

x	P(x)
0	1/6
1	2/6
2	2/6
3	1/6

6.22   Let $y = P(1) = P(2)$, so that
        $2y = P(3)$, $4y = P(4)$, $8y = P(5)$, and $16y = P(6)$. Now
        $P(1) + P(2) + P(3) + P(4) + P(5) + P(6) = 1$, or
        $y + y + 2y + 4y + 8y + 16y = 32y = 1$. Therefore, $y = 1/32$.

x	P(x)
1	1/32
2	1/32
3	2/32
4	4/32
5	8/32
6	16/32

6.23   (a) $\mu = 0(1/8) + 1(3/8) + 2(3/8) + 3(1/8) = 12/8 = 1.5$

        (b) $\sigma^2 = 0^2(1/8) + 1^2(3/8) + 2^2(3/8) + 3^2(1/8) - \mu^2 = 0.75$

        (c) $\sigma = \sqrt{0.75} = 0.866$

        (d)   symmetric

6.24   (a) $\mu = 2(1/4) + 3(1/4) + 4(1/4) + 5(1/4) = 14/4 = 3.5$

        (b) $\sigma^2 = 2^2(1/4) + 3^2(1/4) + 4^2(1/4) + 5^2(1/4) - \mu^2 = 1.25$

        (c) $\sigma = \sqrt{1.25} = 1.118$

        (d)   symmetric

6.25 (a) $\mu = 0(1/10) + 1(2/10) + 2(3/10) + 3(4/10) = 20/10 = 2$

      (b) $\sigma^2 = 0^2(1/10) + 1^2(2/10) + 2^2(3/10) + 3^2(4/10) - \mu^2 = 1$

      (c) $\sigma = \sqrt{1} = 1$

      (d) skewed to the left

6.26 (a) $\mu = 0(4/10) + 1(3/10) + 2(2/10) + 3(1/10) = 10/10 = 1$

      (b) $\sigma^2 = 0^2(4/10) + 1^2(3/10) + 2^2(2/10) + 3^2(1/10) - \mu^2 = 1$

      (c) $\sigma = \sqrt{1} = 1$

      (d) skewed to the right

6.27

x	P(x)	xP(x)	x^2	$x^2 P(x)$
2	1/36	2/36	4	4/36
3	2/36	6/36	9	18/36
4	3/36	12/36	16	48/36
5	4/36	20/36	25	100/36
6	5/36	30/36	36	180/36
7	6/36	42/36	49	294/36
8	5/36	40/36	64	320/36
9	4/36	36/36	81	324/36
10	3/36	30/36	100	300/36
11	2/36	22/36	121	242/36
12	1/36	12/36	144	144/36
Sums:		252/36		1974/36

      (a) $\mu = 252/36 = 7$

      (b) $\sigma^2 = 1974/36 - \mu^2 = 5.8333$

      (c) $\sigma = \sqrt{5.8333} = 2.415$

6.28 (a)

x	P(x)
0	1/10
1	1/10
2	1/10
3	1/10
4	1/10
5	1/10
6	1/10
7	1/10
8	1/10
9	1/10

6.28   (a)   Continued:

x	P(x)	xP(x)	x^2	$x^2P(x)$
0	1/10	0	0	0
1	1/10	1/10	1	1/10
2	1/10	2/10	4	4/10
3	1/10	3/10	9	9/10
4	1/10	4/10	16	16/10
5	1/10	5/10	25	25/10
6	1/10	6/10	36	36/10
7	1/10	7/10	49	49/10
8	1/10	8/10	64	64/10
9	1/10	9/10	81	81/10
	Sums:	45/10		285/10

(b) $\mu = 45/10 = 4.5$

(c) $\sigma^2 = 285/10 - \mu^2 = 8.25$

(d) $\sigma = 2.872$

6.29   (a) $\mu = 1(2/15) + 2(10/15) + 3(2/15) + 4(1/15) = 32/15 = 2.133$

(b) $\sigma^2 = 1^2(2/15) + 2^2(10/15) + 3^2(2/15) + 4^2(1/15) - \mu^2 = 0.516$

(c) $\sigma = \sqrt{0.516} = 0.718$

6.30   (a) $\mu = 0(1/20) + 1(2/20) + 2(3/20) + 3(11/20) + 4(3/20)$
$= 53/20 = 2.65$

(b) $\sigma^2 = 0^2(1/20) + 1^2(2/20) + 2^2(3/20) + 3^2(11/20)$
$+ 4^2(3/20) - \mu^2 = 1.028$

(c) $\sigma = \sqrt{1.028} = 1.014$

6.31 $\mu = 1(1/6) + 2(3/6) + 3(2/6) = 13/6 = 2.167$

$\sigma^2 = 1^2(1/6) + 2^2(3/6) + 3^2(2/6) - \mu^2 = 0.472$

6.32 $\mu = 0(12/13) + 1(1/13) = 1/13 = 0.077$

$\sigma^2 = 0^2(12/13) + 1^2(1/13) - \mu^2 = 0.071$

6.33   Let x be the amount the casino wins.

x	P(x)
1	12/13
-10	1/13

(a) $E(x) = 1(12/13) - 10(1/13) = 2/13 = 15.4$ cents

(b) $26(2/13) = \$4$

6.34   Let x be the amount the casino wins.

x	P(x)
-4	0.493
5	0.507

(a) $E(x) = -4(0.493) + 5(0.507) = 56.3$ cents

(b) $10(56.3) = \$5.63$

6.35   Let x be the amount you win.

x	P(x)
100	1/2000
50	2/2000
25	3/2000
-1	1994/2000

$E(x) = 100(1/2000) + 50(2/2000) + 25(3/2000) - 1(1994/2000)$

$$= -\frac{1719}{2000} = -86 \text{ cents.}$$

6.36   Let x and y be the amount of gain for the bus company for the express and local stops respectively.

x	P(x)		y	P(y)
-500	0.70		-750	0.50
6000	0.30		10000	0.50

$E(x) = -500(0.70) + 6000(0.30) = \$1450$

$E(y) = -750(0.50) + 10000(0.50) = \$4625$

The company should bid on the local stops contract.

6.37   (a)   yes.

(b)   no: the number of trials is not a fixed number.

(c)   no: the trials are dependent.

6.38 $P(x) = \dfrac{3!}{x!(3-x)!}(0.2)^x(0.8)^{3-x}, \; x = 0,1,2,3.$

x	P(x)
0	0.512
1	0.384
2	0.096
3	0.008

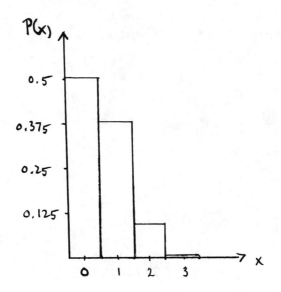

6.39 $P(x) = \dfrac{3!}{x!(3-x)!}(0.8)^x(0.2)^{3-x}, \; x = 0,1,2,3.$

x	P(x)
0	0.008
1	0.096
2	0.384
3	0.512

6.39 Continued:

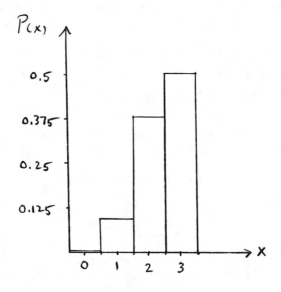

6.40
$$P(x) = \frac{4!}{x!(4-x)!}(0.6)^x(0.4)^{4-x}, \ x = 0,1,2,3,4$$

(a) $P(0) = 0.0256$ (b) $P(3) = 0.3456$

(c) $P(2) = 0.3456$ (d) P(x is at least 2)
                                     = P(2) + P(3) + P(4)
                                     = 0.3456 + 0.3456 + 0.1296
                                     = 0.8208

6.41
$$P(x) = \frac{5!}{x!(5-x)!}(0.8)^x(0.2)^{5-x}, \ x = 0,1,2,3,4,5$$

(a) $P(5) = 0.32768$ (b) $P(0) = 0.00032$ (c) $P(2) = 0.0512$

(d) P(x is at least 4) = P(4) + P(5) = 0.4096 + 0.32768
                                     = 0.73728

6.42 Use table B-2 with $n = 10$, $p = 0.2$.

(a) $P(3) = 0.201$ (b) P(at least 2) = 1-P(less than 2)
                                         = 1-(0.107 + 0.268) = 0.625

(c) The approximate mean number of correct answers is 2, because $\mu = np = 10(0.2) = 2$.

6.43　Use table B-2 with n = 10, p = 0.1.
P(reject shipment) = P(more than 1 defective)
= 1 − P(less than 2 defectives) = 1 − (0.349 + 0.387) = 0.264.

6.44　Use table B-2 with n = 20, p = 0.6.

(a)　P(10) = 0.117.

(b)　P(more than 13 are opposed)
= 0.124 + 0.075 + 0.035 + 0.012 + 0.003 = 0.249.

(c)　P(less than 10 are opposed)
= 0.001 + 0.005 + 0.015 + 0.035 + 0.071 = 0.127.

6.45　Use table B-2 with n = 15, p = 0.4.

(a)　P(7) = 0.177.

(b)　P(less than 4 favor the ban)
= 0.005 + 0.022 + 0.063 = 0.09.

(c)　P(more than 2 favor the ban)
= 1 − P(less than 3 favor the ban)
= 1 − (0.005 + 0.022) = 0.973.

6.46　Use table B-2 with n = 10, p = 0.05.

P(wins a free ticket at least once)
= 1 − P(does not win a free ticket) = 1 − 0.599 = 0.401.

6.47　Use table B-2 with n = 12, p = 0.1.

(a)　P(all cans are acceptable) = 0.282.

(b)　P(more than 2 cans are unacceptable)
= 1 − P(less than 3 cans are unacceptable)
= 1 − (0.282 + 0.377 + 0.230) = 0.111.
The expected number of unacceptable cans, provided
two hundred are selected, is (200)(0.10) = 20.

6.48　(a)　$\mu = np = 20(1/5) = 4.$

(b)　$\sigma^2 = npq = 20(1/5)(4/5) = 3.2.$

(c)　$\sigma = \sqrt{3.2} = 1.789.$

6.49　(a)　$\mu = np = 20(4/5) = 16.$

(b)　$\sigma^2 = npq = 20(4/5)(1/5) = 3.2.$

(c)　$\sigma = \sqrt{3.2} = 1.789.$

6.50　(a)　$\mu = np = 12(1/3) = 4.$

(b)　$\sigma^2 = npq = 12(1/3)(2/3) = 2.667.$

(c)　$\sigma = \sqrt{2.667} = 1.633.$

6.51   (a) $\mu = np = 10(9/10) = 9$

      (b) $\sigma^2 = npq = 10(9/10)(1/10) = 0.9$

      (c) $\sigma = \sqrt{0.9} = 0.949$

6.52   (a) $\mu = np = 13(13/52) = 13/4 = 3.25$

      (b) $\sigma^2 = npq = 13(13/52)(39/52) = 2.438$

      (c) $\sigma = \sqrt{2.438} = 1.561$

6.53   (a) $\mu = np = 100(147/4230) = 3.475$

      (b) $\sigma^2 = npq = 100(147/4230)(4083/4230) = 3.354$

      (c) $\sigma = \sqrt{3.354} = 1.831$

6.54   (a) $\mu = np = 50(0.07) = 3.5$

      (b) $\sigma^2 = npq = 50(0.07)(0.93) = 3.255$

      (c) $\sigma = \sqrt{3.255} = 1.804$

6.55   (a) $\mu = np = 5(2/3) = 3.333$

      (b) $\sigma^2 = npq = 5(2/3)(1/3) = 1.111$

      (c) $\sigma = \sqrt{1.111} = 1.054$

6.56   (a) $\mu = np = 4(5/6) = 3.333$

      (b) $\sigma^2 = npq = 4(5/6)(1/6) = 0.556$

      (c) $\sigma = \sqrt{0.556} = 0.746$

6.57 $\mu = np = 20$ and $\sigma^2 = npq = 4$. Therefore, $\sigma^2 = 20q = 4$ and so $q = 1/5$. Hence $p = 4/5$, and so $\mu = np = n(4/5) = 20$. Therefore, $n = 25$.

6.58 $\mu = np = 100$ and $\sigma^2 = npq = 75$. Therefore, $\sigma^2 = 100q = 75$ and so $q = 3/4$. Hence $p = 1/4$, and so $\mu = np = n(1/4) = 100$. Therefore, $n = 400$.

6.59   (a)   the positive integers   (b)   discrete

6.60   (a)   blood cholesterol, continuous.

      (b)   The population (conceptual) is the collection of all cholesterol level scores of people who will use the diet. The sample is the collection of 50 scores.

6.61   (a)   yes   (b) $\mu = 0(1/4) + 4(3/4) = 3$

      (c) $\sigma^2 = 0^2(1/4) + 4^2(3/4) - \mu^2 = 3$

      (d) $\sigma = \sqrt{3} = 1.732$

6.62   (a)   yes   (b) $\mu = 2(2/3) + 4(1/6) + 6(1/6) = 3$

        (c) $\sigma^2 = 2^2(2/3) + 4^2(1/6) + 6^2(1/6) - \mu^2 = 2.333$

        (d) $\sigma = \sqrt{2.333} = 1.527$

6.63   (a)   no: $\sum P(x) \neq 1$

6.64   (a)   no: $P(4) < 0$

6.65   (a)   yes   (b) $\mu = 3(1) = 3$

        (c) $\sigma^2 = 3^2(1) - 3^2 = 0$ (d) $\sigma = 0$

6.66 $1 = \sum P(x) = c + 2c + 3c + 4c = 10c$.   So $c = 1/10$

6.67 $1 = \sum P(x) = c + 2c = 3c$.   So $c = 1/3$.

6.68 $1 = \sum P(x) = c/6 + 2c/6 = 3c/6$.   So $c = 2$.

6.69   (a)

x	P(x)
0	11/13
1	2/13

            (b) $\mu = 0(11/13) + 1(2/13) = 2/13 = 0.154$

        (c) $\sigma^2 = 0^2(11/13) + 1^2(2/13) - \mu^2 = 0.13$

        (d) $\sigma = \sqrt{0.13} = 0.361$

6.70   (a)   Note that x is a binomial random variable with $n = 3$ and $p = 0.4$. Using table B-2, the probability distribution is as follows:

x	P(x)
0	0.216
1	0.432
2	0.288
3	0.064

        (b) $\mu = np = 3(0.4) = 1.2$

        (c) $\sigma^2 = npq = 3(0.4)(0.6) = 0.72$

        (d) $\sigma = \sqrt{0.72} = 0.849$

6.71   The six possible outcomes along with the value of x are:

outcome	x
123	3
132	1
213	1
231	0
312	0
321	1

6.71   (a)
x	P(x)
0	2/6
1	3/6
3	1/6

(b) $\mu = 0(2/6) + 1(3/6) + 3(1/6) = 1$

(c) $\sigma^2 = 0^2(2/6) + 1^2(3/6) + 3^2(1/6) - \mu^2 = 1$ (d) $\sigma = 1$

6.72

x	P(x)	xP(x)	x^2	$x^2 P(x)$
0	0.3679	0	0	0
1	0.3679	0.3679	1	0.3679
2	0.1839	0.3678	4	0.7356
3	0.0613	0.1839	9	0.5517
4	0.0153	0.0612	16	0.2448
5	0.0031	0.0155	25	0.0775
6	0.0005	0.0030	36	0.0180
7	0.0001	0.0007	49	0.0049
Sums:		1		2.0004

(a) $\mu = 1$ (b) $\sigma^2 = 2.0004 - 1 = 1.0004$

(c) $\sigma = \sqrt{1.0004} = 1.0002$

(d)

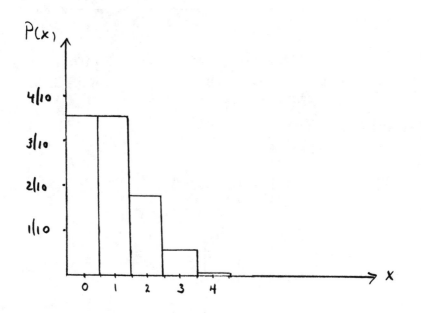

6.73　$q^4 = P(0) = 0.2401$, so $q = 0.7$.　Therefore $p = 0.3$.

(a)　$\mu = np = 4(0.3) = 1.2$.

(b)　$\sigma^2 = npq = 4(0.3)(0.7) = 0.84$.

(c)　$\sigma = \sqrt{0.84} = 0.917$.

(d)

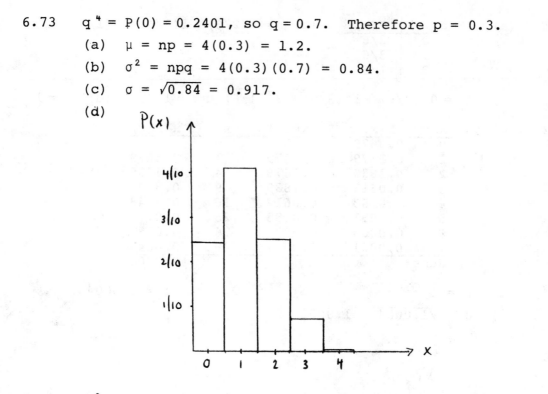

6.74　$q^2 = P(0) = 0.36$, so that $q = 0.6$.　Therefore, $p = 0.4$.

(a)　$\mu = np = 2(0.4) = 0.8$.　　(b)　$\sigma^2 = npq = 2(0.4)(0.6) = 0.48$

(c)　$\sigma = \sqrt{0.48} = 0.693$

(d)

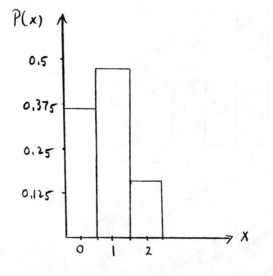

6.75

x	P(x)	xP(x)	x^2	$x^2P(x)$
11	0.3	3.3	121	36.3
12	0.25	3	144	36
13	0.1	1.3	169	16.9
14	0.1	1.4	196	19.6
15	0.2	3	225	45
16	0.05	0.8	256	12.8
Sums:		12.8		166.6

(a) $\mu = 12.8$ (b) $\sigma^2 = 166.6 - \mu^2 = 2.76$

(c) $\sigma = \sqrt{2.76} = 1.661$

(d)

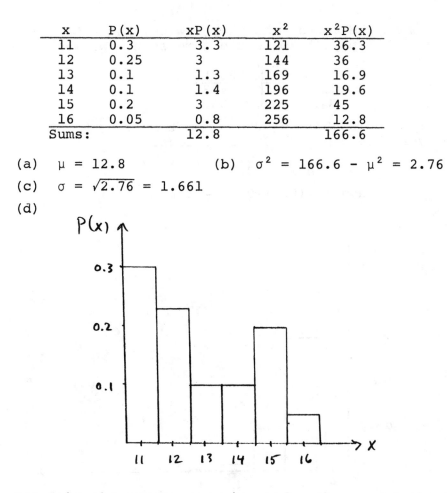

6.76   Let x be the amount you win, and y the amount the friend should pay to make the game even. We want E(x) = 0.

x	P(x)
-10	1/13
- 5	2/13
y	10/13

Now E(x) = 0 = -10(1/13) - 5(2/13) + y(10/13)
         = -20/13 + 10y/13. Therefore, y = $2.

6.77   Let x be the amount the player wins.

x	P(x)
35	1/37
-1	36/37

E(x) = 35(1/37) - 1(36/37) = -2.7 cents.

6.78   Let x be the amount the player wins, and y the amount
       the player pays to make the game even. We want $E(x) = 0$.

x	P(x)
4	0.493
y	0.507

$E(x) = 0 = 4(0.493) + y(0.507)$, so that $y = -\$3.89$. The
player should pay \$3.89 for a loss.

6.79   (a) $\mu = np = 7(0.1) = 0.7$

            $\sigma^2 = npq = 7(0.1)(0.9) = 0.63$

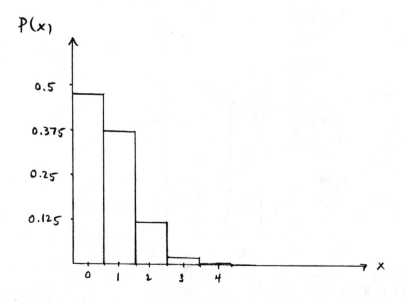

The distribution is skewed to the right.

6.79 (b) $\mu = np = 7(0.9) = 6.3$
$\sigma^2 = npq = 7(0.9)(0.1) = 0.63$

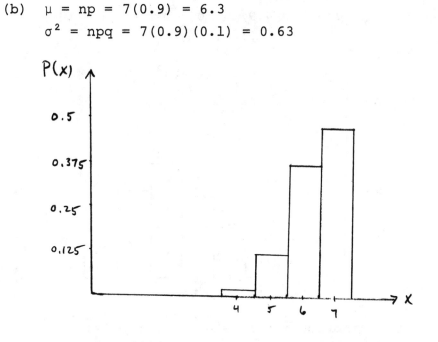

The distribution is skewed to the left.

(c) $\mu = np = 7(0.3) = 2.1.$ $\sigma^2 = npq = 7(0.3)(0.7) = 1.47.$

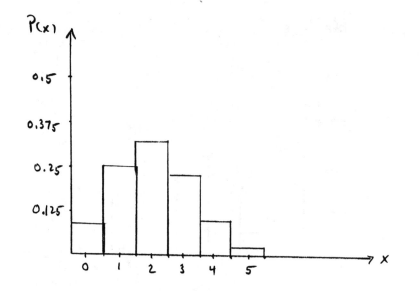

The distribution is skewed to the right.

6.79   (d) $\mu = np = 7(0.7) = 4.9$. $\sigma^2 = npq = 7(0.7)(0.3) = 1.47$.

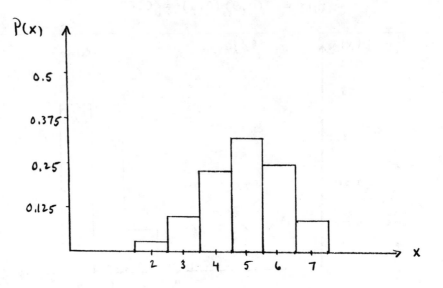

The distribution is skewed to the left.

(e) $\mu = np = 7(0.5) = 3.5$. $\sigma^2 = npq = 7(0.5)(0.5) = 1.75$.

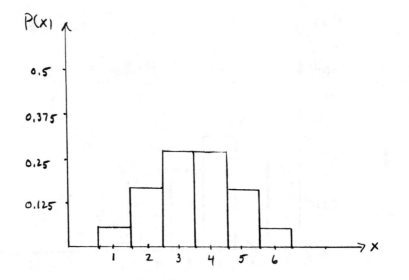

The distribution is symmetric.

100

6.80   Use table B-2 with n = 12, p = 0.4.

    (a) P(at least 8 will be cured)
        = 0.042 + 0.012 + 0.002 = 0.056.

    (b) P(at least 1 will be cured) = 1 − P(none is cured)
        = 1 − 0.002 = 0.998.

6.81   Use table B-2 with n = 6, p = 0.5.

    (a)   P(3 boys) = 0.312.   (b)   P(6 boys) = 0.016.

    (c)   P(6 boys or 6 girls) = 2(0.016) = 0.032.

    (d)   P(at least 1 boy) = 1 − P(6 girls) = 1 − 0.016 = 0.984.

6.82   Use table B-2 with n = 15, p = 0.3.

    (a)   P(4 are independent) = 0.219.

    (b)   P(no more than 3 are independent)
        = 0.005 + 0.031 + 0.092 + 0.17 = 0.298.

    (c)   P(at least 10 are independent) = 0.003 + 0.001 = 0.004.

6.83   Use $P(x) = \dfrac{5!}{x!(5-x)!}(0.85)^x(0.15)^{5-x}, x = 0,1,2,3,4,5.$

    (a)   P(5) = 0.444.

    (b)   P(at least 3 will need repairs)
        = P(at most 2 will not need repair)
        = 0.002 + 0.024 = 0.026.

6.84   Use table B-2 with n = 7 and p = 21/30 = 0.7.

    (a)   P(all red) = 0.082.   (b)   P(1 red) = 0.004.

    (c)   P(no more than 2 are red) = 0.004 + 0.025 = 0.029.

6.85   (a) $\mu = np = 12(0.4) = 4.8.$

    (b) $\sigma^2 = npq = 12(0.4)(0.6) = 2.88.$

    (c) $\sigma = \sqrt{2.88} = 1.697.$

6.86   (a) $\mu = np = 6(0.5) = 3.$

    (b) $\sigma^2 = npq = 6(0.5)(0.5) = 1.5.$

    (c) $\sigma = \sqrt{1.5} = 1.225.$

6.87   (a) $\mu = np = 15(0.3) = 4.5$.

         (b) $\sigma^2 = npq = 15(0.3)(0.7) = 3.15$.

         (c) $\sigma = \sqrt{3.15} = 1.775$.

6.88   (a) $\mu = np = 5(0.85) = 4.25$.

         (b) $\sigma^2 = npq = 5(0.85)(0.15) = 0.638$.

         (c) $\sigma = \sqrt{0.638} = 0.799$.

6.89   (a) $\mu = np = 7(0.7) = 4.9$

         (b) $\sigma^2 = npq = 7(0.7)(0.3) = 1.47$.

         (c) $\sigma = \sqrt{1.47} = 1.212$.

Chapter 7

4821 4505
.5
.982/-.9605

7.1 (a) The area of the rectangle is 1.   Therefore,
          (120)h = 1   or   h = 1/120.

     (b)   (i)   P(0 < x < 30) = 30/120 = 0.25.

            (ii) P(x > 75) = (120 - 75)/120 = 0.375.   .0316

            (iii) P(45 < x < 60) = (60 - 45)/120 = 0.125.

            (iv) P(x < 15 or x > 90) = P(x < 15) + P(x > 90)
                  = 15/120 + (120 - 90)/120 = 0.375.

     (c) (i) P(x < 30),   (ii) P(x > 75),   (iii) P(45 < x < 60)

7.2 (a) (0.393 + 0.239)(100) = 63.2%.

     (b) (0.145 + 0.088)(100) = 23.3%.

     (c) [1 - (0.393 + 0.239 + 0.145 + 0.088 + 0.053 + 0.032)](100)
          = 5%.

     (d) (0.088 + 0.053 + 0.032 + 0.05)(100) = 22.3%.

     (e) (0.053 + 0.032 + 0.05)(100) = 13.5%.

7.3 (a) P(x > 700) = P(x < 300) = 0.5 - (0.1359 + 0.3413) = 0.0228.
          Therefore, P(x > 700 or x < 300) = P(x > 700) + P(x < 300)
          = 2(0.0228) = 0.0456.

     (b) 0.3413 + 0.1359 + 0.0228 = 0.5.   (c)   0.1359.

     (d) 0.5 + 0.3413 = 0.8413.

     (e) 0.1359 + 0.3413 = 0.4772.   (f)   2(0.3413) = 0.6826.

     (g) 2(0.1359 + 0.3413) = 0.9544.

7.4 (a) 0.5.   (b) 0.2486.   (c) 0.2486.

     (d) 0.4821 - 0.4505 = 0.0316   (e)   0.4893 - 0.4265 = 0.0628

     (f) 0.4821 + 0.4452 = 0.9273   (g)   0.2673 + 0.4896 = 0.7569.

     (h) 0.4686 + 0.5000 = 0.9686   (i)   0.5000 + 0.4750 = 0.9750.

     (j) 2(0.5000 - 0.4772) = 0.0456 (k)   2(0.3413) = 0.6826.

     (ℓ) 2(0.4772) = 0.9544   (m)   2(0.4987) = 0.9974.

7.5 (a) 2   (b) -1.5   (c) 1.72   (d) -1.24

     (e) 0   (f) 1.41   (g) -1.75   (h) -2.45

7.6 (a) 2.33   (b) -1.65   (c) -1.28   (d) 2.58

     (e) 0.84

7.7   (a) $P(x > 46) = P(z > \frac{46-46}{4}) = P(z > 0) = 0.5$, or 50%.

(b) $P(x > 50) = P(z > \frac{50-46}{4}) = P(z > 1) = 0.5 - 0.3413 = 0.1587$, or
$$15.87\%$$

(c) $P(x > 40) = P(z > \frac{40-46}{4}) = P(z > -1.5) = 0.4332 + 0.5 = 0.9332$,
$$\text{or } 93.32\%$$

(d) $P(x < 38) = P(z < \frac{38-46}{4}) = P(z < -2) = 0.5 - 0.4772 = 0.0228$, or
$$2.28\%$$

(e) $P(x < 49) = P(z < \frac{49-46}{4}) = P(z < 0.75) = 0.5 + 0.2734 = 0.7734$, or
$$77.34\%$$

(f) $P(45 < x < 49) = P(\frac{45-46}{4} < z < \frac{49-46}{4}) = P(-0.25 < z < 0.75)$

$$= 0.0987 + 0.2734 = 0.3721, \text{ or } 37.21\%.$$

(g) $P(50 < x < 54) = P(\frac{50-46}{4} < z < \frac{54-46}{4}) = P(1 < z < 2)$

$$= 0.4772 - 0.3413 = 0.1359, \text{ or } 13.59\%$$

(h) $P(x > 56 \text{ or } x < 46) = P(z > \frac{56-46}{4}) + P(z < \frac{46-46}{4})$

$$= P(z > 2.5) + P(z < 0)$$

$$= (0.5 - 0.4938) + 0.5 = 0.5062,$$

$$\text{or } 50.62\%.$$

(i) $P(-1.5 < z < 1.5) = 2P(0 < z < 1.5) = 2(0.4332) = 0.8664$,
$$\text{or } 86.64\%.$$

(j) $P(z < -2.3 \text{ or } z > 2.3) = 2P(z > 2.3) = 2(0.5 - 0.4893)$
$$= 0.0214, \text{ or } 2.14\%.$$

7.8   (a) $500 + (1.65)(100) = 665$.

(b) $500 - (0.53)(100) = 447$; $500 + (0.53)(100) = 553$.

(c)   P(randomly selected student > 650) $= P(z > \frac{650 - 500}{100})$
$$= P(z > 1.5) = 0.5 - 0.4332 = 0.0668.$$

The number of students expected to score more than
650 is $(1000)(0.0668) \doteq 67$.

7.9   (a) $P(x < 60) = P(z < \frac{60-96}{18}) = P(z < -2) = 0.5 - 0.4772 = 0.0228$,
or 2.28%.

(b) $96 + (-2.33)(18) \doteq 54$.

7.10 (a) $P(x < 10) = P(z < \frac{10 - 15}{4}) = P(z < -1.25) = 0.5 - 0.3944 = 0.1056$

(b) $0.2 = P(z < -0.84) = P[x < 15 - (0.84)4] = P(x < 11.64)$, so about 11.64 minutes.

(c) 11:15

7.11 (a) $700 + (1.28)(70) = 789.6$.

(b) $850 = 800 + (0.84)\sigma$, so $\sigma = \frac{850-800}{0.84} = 59.5$

7.12 (a) $0.035 + 0.01 + 0.002 = 0.047$

(b) $\mu = np = (13)(0.5) = 6.5$
$\sigma^2 = npq = (13)(0.5)(0.5) = 3.25$
$\sigma = \sqrt{3.25} = 1.8$
$P(\text{at least 10 successes}) \doteq P(z > \frac{9.5 - 6.5}{1.8})$
$= P(z > 1.67) = 0.5 - 0.4525 = 0.0475$.

7.13 (a) $0.003 + 0.015 + 0.047 + 0.101 + 0.162 + 0.198 + 0.189 = 0.715$

(b) $\mu = np = (16)(0.4) = 6.4$
$\sigma^2 = npq = (16)(0.4)(0.6) = 3.84$
$\sigma = \sqrt{3.84} = 1.96$
$P(\text{at most 7 successes}) \doteq P(z < \frac{7.5 - 6.4}{1.96}) = P(z < 0.56)$
$= 0.5 + 0.2123 = 0.7123$.

7.14 (a) 0.192 (b) $\mu = np = 20(0.7) = 14$
$\sigma^2 = npq = (20)(0.7)(0.3) = 4.2$
$\sigma = \sqrt{4.2} = 2.05$
$P(14 \text{ successes}) \doteq P(\frac{13.5 - 14}{2.05} < z < \frac{14.5 - 14}{2.05})$
$= P(-0.24 < z < 0.24) = 2(0.0948) = 0.1896$

7.15 (a) $0.024 + 0.061 + 0.118 = 0.203$

(b) $\mu = np = (15)(0.6) = 9$
$\sigma^2 = npq = (15)(0.6)(0.4) = 3.6$
$\sigma = 1.90$

P(between 5 and 7 successes inclusive) $\doteq P(\frac{4.5-9}{1.90} < z < \frac{7.5-9}{1.90})$

$= P(-2.37 < z < -0.79) = 0.4911 - 0.2852 = 0.2059$

7.16 (a) $1 - (0.014 + 0.003 + 0.001) = 1 - 0.018 = 0.982$

(b) $\mu = np = (14)(0.4) = 5.6$
$\sigma^2 = npq = (14)(0.4)(0.6) = 3.36$
$\sigma = \sqrt{3.36} = 1.83$

P(no more than 9 successes) $\doteq P(z < \frac{9.5 - 5.6}{1.83} = 2.13)$

$= 0.5 + 0.4834 = 0.9834$

7.17 (a) 0.016 (b) $\mu = np = (12)(0.5) = 6$
$\sigma^2 = npq = (12)(0.5)(0.5) = 3$
$\sigma = \sqrt{3} = 1.73$

P(10 successes) $\doteq P(\frac{9.5 - 6}{1.73} < z < \frac{10.5 - 6}{1.73})$

$= P(2.02 < z < 2.60) = 0.4953 - 0.4783 = 0.017$

7.18 $\mu = np = (1600)(0.04) = 64$
$\sigma^2 = npq = (1600)(0.04)(0.96) = 61.44$
$\sigma = \sqrt{61.44} = 7.84$

P(no more than 45 defectives) $\doteq P(z < \frac{45.5 - 64}{7.84})$

$= P(z < -2.36) = 0.5 - 0.4909 = 0.0091$

7.19 $\mu = np = (100)(0.25) = 25$
$\sigma^2 = npq = (100)(0.25)(0.75) = 18.75$
$\sigma = \sqrt{18.75} = 4.33$

P(at least 35 correct answers) $\doteq P(z > \frac{34.5 - 25}{4.33})$

$= P(z > 2.19) = 0.5 - 0.4857 = 0.0143$

7.20 $\mu = np = (1600)(0.5) = 800.$

    $\sigma^2 = npq = (1600)(0.5)(0.5) = 400.$ $\sigma = \sqrt{400} = 20.$

  (a) P(between 760 and 840 heads inclusive)

    $\doteq P(\frac{759.5 - 800}{20} < z < \frac{840.5 - 800}{20})$

    $= P(-2.03 < z < 2.03) = 2(0.4788) = 0.9576$

  (b) P(at least 790 heads) $\doteq P(z > \frac{789.5 - 800}{20}) = P(z > -0.53)$

        $= 0.2019 + 0.5 = 0.7019$

  (c) P(800 heads) $\doteq P(\frac{799.5 - 800}{20} < z < \frac{800.5 - 800}{20})$

    $= P(-0.03 < z < 0.03) = 2(0.0120) = 0.024$

  (d) P(less than 731 heads) $\doteq P(z < \frac{730.5 - 800}{20})$

    $= P(z < -3.48) = 0.5 - 0.4997 = 0.0003.$

It does appear that the coin is biased toward tails.

7.21   (a) $\mu = np = (400)(0.6) = 240.$

      $\sigma^2 = npq = (400)(0.6)(0.4) = 96.$ $\sigma = \sqrt{96} = 9.8.$

P(less than 220 voters support her decision)

$\doteq P(z < \frac{219.5 - 240}{9.8}) = P(z < -2.09) = 0.5 - 0.4817 = 0.0183$

  (b) P(less than 211 voters support her decision)

    $\doteq P(z < \frac{210.5 - 240}{9.8}) = P(z < -3.01) = 0.5 - 0.4987 = 0.0013.$

The data do not support the official's claim.

7.22 $\mu = np = (195)(0.5) = 97.5.$ $\sigma^2 = npq = (195)(0.5)(0.5) = 48.75$

    $\sigma = \sqrt{48.75} = 6.98.$

P(at least 120 girls) $\doteq P(z > \frac{119.5 - 97.5}{6.98} = P(z > 3.15)$

$= 0.5 - 0.4992 = 0.0008.$ The data support the claim.

7.23 (a)

$\bar{x}$	$P(\bar{x})$
0	1/9
1	2/9
2	3/9
3	2/9
4	1/9

(b) $\mu_{\bar{x}} = 0(1/9) + 1(2/9) + 2(3/9) + 3(2/9) + 4(1/9) = 2$

$\sigma^2_{\bar{x}} = 0^2(1/9) + 1^2(2/9) + 2^2(3/9) + 3^2(2/9) + 4^2(1/9) - \mu^2_{\bar{x}} = 4/3$

(c) $\mu_x = 0(1/3) + 2(1/3) + 4(1/3) = 2 = \mu_{\bar{x}}$

$\sigma^2_x = 0^2(1/3) + 2^2(1/3) + 4^2(1/3) - \mu^2_x = 8/3 = n\sigma^2_{\bar{x}}$

7.24 (a) $\mu_x = 1(1/6) + 2(2/6) + 3(3/6) = 14/6 = 7/3.$

$\sigma^2_x = 1^2(1/6) + 2^2(2/6) + 3^2(3/6) - \mu^2_x = 6 - (7/3)^2 = 5/9.$

(b) 3,1

(c) $\mu_{\bar{x}} = \mu_x = 7/3.$ $\qquad \sigma^2_{\bar{x}} = \sigma^2_x/n = \dfrac{(5/9)}{49} = 0.0113.$

(d) approximately normal.

7.25 (a) $\mu_{\bar{x}} = \mu_x = 200.$ $\qquad$ (b) $\sigma^2_{\bar{x}} = (100)^2/100 = 100$, so that

$$\sigma_{\bar{x}} = 10.$$

(c) $P(195 < \bar{x} < 205) = P(\dfrac{195 - 200}{10} < z < \dfrac{205 - 200}{10})$

$= P(-0.5 < z < 0.5) = 2(0.1915) = 0.3830.$

(d) $P(\bar{x} > 210) = P(z > \dfrac{210-200}{10}) = P(z > 1) = 0.5 - 0.3413 = 0.1587.$

(e) $P(195 < x < 205) = P(\dfrac{195-200}{100} < z < \dfrac{205-200}{100})$

$= P(-0.05 < z < 0.05) = 2(0.0199) = 0.0398.$

(f) $P(x > 210) = P(z > \dfrac{210-200}{100}) = P(z > 0.10) = 0.5 - 0.0398$

$= 0.4602.$

7.26 (a) $\mu_{\bar{x}} = \mu_x = 200$. (b) $\sigma_{\bar{x}}^2 = (100)^2/400 = 25$, so that $\sigma_{\bar{x}} = 5$.

(c) $P(195 < \bar{x} < 205) = P(\frac{195-200}{5} < z < \frac{205-200}{5}) = P(-1 < z < 1)$

$$= 2(0.3413) = 0.6826.$$

(d) $P(\bar{x} > 210) = P(z > \frac{210-200}{5}) = P(z > 2) = 0.5 - 0.4772 = 0.0228.$

7.27 $\mu_{\bar{x}} = 510$. $\sigma_{\bar{x}}^2 = (90)^2/100 = 81$, so that $\sigma_{\bar{x}} = 9$.

(a) $P(\bar{x} > 530) = P(z > \frac{530-510}{9}) = P(z > 2.22) = 0.5 - 0.4868 = 0.0132.$

(b) $P(\bar{x} < 500) = P(z < \frac{500-510}{9}) = P(z < -1.11) = 0.5 - 0.3665 = 0.1335.$

(c) $P(495 < \bar{x} < 515) = P(\frac{495-510}{9} < z < \frac{515-510}{9}) = P(-1.67 < z < 0.56)$

$$= 0.4525 + 0.2123 = 0.6648.$$

7.28 $\mu_{\bar{x}} = \mu_x = 18500$. $\sigma_{\bar{x}}^2 = (2000)^2/75 = 53333.33$, so that
$\sigma_{\bar{x}} = \sqrt{53333.33} = 230.94$.

$P(\bar{x} > 19000) = P(z > \frac{19000-18500}{230.94}) = P(z > 2.17) = 0.5 - 0.4850 = 0.0150.$

7.29 $\mu_{\bar{x}} = \mu_x = 1200$. $\sigma_{\bar{x}}^2 = (120)^2/35 = 411.43$, so that $\sigma_{\bar{x}} = \sqrt{411.43} = 20.28$.

$P(\bar{x} < 1160) = P(z < \frac{1160-1200}{20.28}) = P(z < -1.97) = 0.5 - 0.4756 = 0.0244.$

7.30 $\mu_{\bar{x}} = \mu_x = 74$. $\sigma_{\bar{x}}^2 = (14)^2/50 = 3.92$, so that $\sigma_{\bar{x}} = \sqrt{3.92} = 1.98$.

(a) $P(\bar{x} \geq 76) = P(z \geq \frac{76-74}{1.98}) = P(z \geq 1.01) = 0.5 - 0.3438 = 0.1562.$

(b) No, for if the teacher's claim were true, there are about 156 chances in 1000 of observing a more extreme value than what was observed.

7.31 (a) $1 - (0.2031+0.1455+0.1043+0.0747+0.0535+0.1354)=0.2835$

(b) 0.1354 (c) $0.2031 + 0.1455 = 0.3486$

(d) $1 - 0.2835 = 0.7165$ (e) $1 - 0.1455 = 0.8545$

7.32 (a) 1

(b) $1-(0.3935+0.2387+0.1447+0.0878+0.0533+0.0323) = 0.0497$

(c) $0.1447 + 0.0878 = 0.2325$ (d) $1 - 0.3935 = 0.6065$

(e) $0.3935 + 0.2387 = 0.6322$

7.33 (a) $1/8 = (1/2)(1/2)h$, so that $h = 1/2$.

(b)   For $0 \le x \le 1/2$, $y = f(x) = x$. Note: For $0 \le x \le 1/2$, the line passes through $(0,0)$ and $(1/2,1/2)$. For $1/2 \le x \le 9/4$, $y = f(x) = 1/2$.

(c) $P(1/2 < x < 9/4) = \frac{1}{2}(9/4 - 1/2) = 7/8$.

(d) $P(1 < x < 9/4) = (1/2)(9/4 - 1) = 5/8$.

(e) $P(0 < x < 7/4) = P(0 < x < 1/2) + P(1/2 < x < 7/4)$
                    $= (1/2)^3 + (1/2)(7/4 - 1/2) = 3/4$

(f) $P(0 \le x < \frac{1}{4}) = 1/2(1/4)^2 = 1/32$.

7.34 (a) $P(0 < x < 1) = 1 - P(1 < x < 2) = 1 - (1/2)(1)(1/2) = 3/4$

(b) $P(1/2 < x < 1) = (1/2)(3/4) - (1/2)^2(3/4 - 1/2) = 5/16$

(c) $P(x > 3/2) = (1/2)^2(1/4) = 1/16$

(d) $P(x < 1/2) = 1 - P(x > 1/2) = 1 - (1/2)(3/2)(3/4) = 7/16$

7.35 (a) $1000P(z > 2) = (1000)(0.5 - 0.4772) \doteq 23$

(b) $1000P(z < 1.5) = (1000)(0.5 + 0.4332) \doteq 933$

(c) $1000P(-1.2 < z < -1.1) = (1000)(0.3849 - 0.3643) \doteq 21$

(d) $1000P(z < -1) = (1000)(0.5 - 0.3413) \doteq 159$

(e) $1000P(z > 2.5$ or $z < -2.5) = (2000)(0.5 - 0.4938) \doteq 12$

(f) $1000P(z > 3$ or $z < -3) = (2000)(0.5 - 0.4987) \doteq 3$

7.36 (a) 1.96 (b) 0.67 (c) 0 (d) -1.04

7.37 (a) $100P(x < 170) = 100P(z < \frac{170-160}{10}) = 100P(z < 1)$
        $= 100(0.5 + 0.3413) = 84.13\%$.

(b) $160 + (1.65)(10) = 176.5$ minutes.

7.38　(a)　$100P(x < 7) = 100P(z < \frac{7 - 12}{2.5}) = 100P(z < -2)$

$= 100(0.5 - 0.4772) = 2.28\%.$

(b)　$100P(x > 14) = 100P(z > \frac{14-12}{2.5}) = 100P(z > 0.8)$

$= 100(0.5 - 0.2881) = 21.19\%.$

(c)　$12 + (-1.65)(2.5) = 7.88$ years.

7.39　P(brand A lasts longer than 980 days)

$= P(z > \frac{980 - 1000}{30}) = P(z > -0.67) = 0.5 + 0.2486 = 0.7486$

P(brand B lasts longer than 980 days) $= P(z > \frac{980 - 990}{10})$

$= P(z > -1) = 0.5 + 0.3413 = 0.8413$

Buy brand B.

7.40　(a)　$0.002 + 0.013 + 0.046 + 0.105 = 0.166$

(b)　$\mu = np = (18)(0.3) = 5.4$

$\sigma^2 = npq = (18)(0.3)(0.7) = 3.78$　　　$\sigma = \sqrt{3.78} = 1.94$

P(no more than 3 successes) $\doteq P(z < \frac{3.5 - 5.4}{1.94})$

$= P(z < -0.98) = 0.5 - 0.3365 = 0.1635$

7.41　(a)　$0.142+0.189+0.198+0.162+0.101+0.047+0.015+0.003=0.857$

(b)　$\mu = np = (16)(0.6) = 9.6$

$\sigma^2 = npq = (16)(0.6)(0.4) = 3.84.$　　　$\sigma = \sqrt{3.84} = 1.96$

P(at least 8 successes) $\doteq P(z > \frac{7.5 - 9.6}{1.96}) = P(z > -1.07)$

$= 0.5 + 0.3577 = 0.8577$

7.42　(a)　0.196

(b)　$\mu = np = (15)(0.5) = 7.5.$

$\sigma^2 = npq = (15)(0.5)(0.5) = 3.75.$　　　$\sigma = 1.94$

P(7 successes) $\doteq P(\frac{6.5 - 7.5}{1.94} < z < \frac{7.5 - 7.5}{1.94})$

$= P(-0.52 < z < 0) = 0.1985$

7.43 (a) $0.004 + 0.012 + 0.031 + 0.065 + 0.114 = 0.226$

(b) $\mu = np = (20)(0.7) = 14.$

$\sigma^2 = npq = (20)(0.7)(0.3) = 4.2 \qquad \sigma = 2.05.$

P(between 8 and 12 successes inclusive)

$\doteq P(\frac{7.5 - 14}{2.05} < z < \frac{12.5 - 14}{2.05}) = P(-3.17 < z < -0.73)$

$= 0.4992 - 0.2673 = 0.2319.$

7.44 (a) $0.003 + 0.016 + 0.054 + 0.121 + 0.193 = 0.387$

(b) $\mu = np = (12)(0.5) = 6. \qquad \sigma^2 = npq = (12)(0.5)(0.5) = 3.$

$\sigma = \sqrt{3} = 1.73.$

P(no more than 5 successes) $\doteq P(z < \frac{5.5 - 6}{1.73}) = P(z < -0.29)$

$= 0.5 - 0.1141 = 0.3859.$

7.45 (a) $0.196 + 0.175 + 0.122 + 0.067 = 0.560.$

(b) $\mu = np = (16)(0.5) = 8. \quad \sigma^2 = npq = (16)(0.5)(0.5) = 4.$

$\sigma = \sqrt{4} = 2.$

P(between 8 and 11 successes inclusive)

$\doteq P(\frac{7.5 - 8}{2} < z < \frac{11.5 - 8}{2}) = P(-0.25 < z < 1.75)$

$= 0.0987 + 0.4599 = 0.5586.$

7.46 $\mu = np = (400)(0.5) = 200. \quad \sigma^2 = npq = (400)(0.5)(0.5) = 100.$

$\sigma = \sqrt{100} = 10.$

(a) $P(x \geq 210) \doteq P(z \geq \frac{209.5 - 200}{10}) = P(z \geq 0.95)$

$= 0.5 - 0.3289 = 0.1711$

(b) $P(180 \leq x \leq 220) \doteq P(\frac{179.5 - 200}{10} \leq z \leq \frac{220.5 - 200}{10})$

$= P(-2.05 \leq z \leq 2.05) = 2(0.4798) = 0.9596$

(c) $P(170 \leq x \leq 230) \doteq P(\frac{169.5 - 200}{10} \leq z \leq \frac{230.5 - 200}{10})$

$= P(-3.05 \leq z \leq 3.05) = 2(0.4989) = 0.9978.$

(d) $P(x < 185) \doteq P(z < \frac{184.5 - 200}{10}) = P(z < -1.55)$

$= 0.5 - 0.4394 = 0.0606.$

7.46 (e) $P(x = 200) \doteq P(\frac{199.5 - 200}{10} < z < \frac{200.5 - 200}{10})$

$= P(-0.05 < z < 0.05) = 2(0.0199) = 0.0398.$

(f) $P(x = 210) \doteq P(\frac{209.5 - 200}{10} < z < \frac{210.5 - 200}{10})$

$= P(0.95 < z < 1.05) = 0.3531 - 0.3289 = 0.0242.$

7.47 $\mu = np = (315)(0.92) = 289.8.$

$\sigma^2 = npq = (315)(0.92)(0.08) = 23.18.$ $\qquad \sigma = \sqrt{23.18} = 4.81.$

P(at most 300 passengers show up)

$\doteq P(z < \frac{300.5 - 289.8}{4.81}) = P(z < 2.22) = 0.5 + 0.4868 = 0.9868.$

7.48 (a) $\mu_{\overline{x}} = \mu_x = 66.$ $\qquad$ (b) $\sigma_{\overline{x}}^2 = 3^2/100,$ so that $\sigma_{\overline{x}} = \frac{3}{10} = 0.3.$

(c) $100P(\overline{x} > 66.5) = 100P(z > \frac{66.5 - 66}{0.3}) = 100P(z > 1.67)$

$= 100(0.5 - 0.4525) = 4.75\%.$

(d) $100P(x > 66.5) = 100P(z > \frac{66.5 - 66}{3}) = 100P(z > 0.17)$

$= 100(0.5 - 0.0675) = 43.25\%.$

7.49 (a) $P(x > 72) = P(z > \frac{72 - 70}{3}) = P(z > 0.67)$

$= 0.5000 - 0.2486 = 0.2514.$

(b) $P(x < 73) = P(z < \frac{73 - 70}{3}) = P(z < 1) = 0.5 + 0.3413$

$= 0.8413.$

(c) $P(66 < x < 74) = P(\frac{66 - 70}{3} < z < \frac{74 - 70}{3})$

$= P(-1.33 < z < 1.33) = 2(0.4082) = 0.8164.$

(d) $P(65 < x < 70) = P(\frac{65 - 70}{3} < z < \frac{70 - 70}{3})$

$= P(-1.67 < z < 0) = 0.4525.$

Now $\mu_{\overline{x}} = \mu_x = 70.$ Also $\sigma_{\overline{x}}^2 = 9/36,$ so that $\sigma_{\overline{x}} = \sqrt{\frac{9}{36}} = 0.5.$

(e) $P(69 < \overline{x} < 71) = P(\frac{69 - 70}{0.5} < z < \frac{71 - 70}{0.5}) = P(-2 < z < 2)$

$= 2(0.4772) = 0.9544.$

7.49   (f) $P(\bar{x} < 69.5) = P(z < \dfrac{69.5 - 70}{0.5}) = P(z < -1)$

           $= 0.5 - 0.3413 = 0.1587.$

  (g) $P(\bar{x} > 71) = P(z > \dfrac{71 - 70}{0.5}) = P(z > 2) = 0.5 - 0.4772$

                                          $= 0.0228.$

  (h) $P(70 < \bar{x} < 71.5) = P(\dfrac{70 - 70}{0.5} < z < \dfrac{71.5 - 70}{0.5})$

                         $= P(0 < z < 3) = 0.4987.$

7.50   (a) $100P(x < 126) = 100P(z < \dfrac{126 - 128}{1}) = 100P(z < -2)$

                        $= 100(0.5 - 0.4772) = 2.28\%.$

  (b) $100P(x > 129) = 100P(z > \dfrac{129 - 128}{1}) = 100P(z > 1)$

                        $= 100(0.5 - 0.3413) = 15.87\%.$

  (c) $100P(127.5 < x < 130.5) = 100P(\dfrac{127.5 - 128}{1} < z < \dfrac{130.5 - 128}{1})$

      $= 100P(-0.5 < z < 2.5) = 100(0.1915 + 0.4938) = 68.53\%.$

      Now $\mu_{\bar{x}} = \mu_x = 128.$ Also $\sigma^2_{\bar{x}} = 1/25$, so that

      $\sigma_{\bar{x}} = \sqrt{\dfrac{1}{25}} = 0.2.$

  (d) $P(\bar{x} \leq 127.4) = P(z < \dfrac{127.4 - 128}{0.2}) = P(z < -3)$

                      $= 0.5 - 0.4987 = 0.0013.$

  (e) Yes. The probability of observing a sample mean as small or smaller than 127.4 is very small.

7.51

x	P(x)	xP(x)	x^2	$x^2P(x)$
0	1/10	0	0	0
1	1/10	1/10	1	1/10
2	1/10	2/10	4	4/10
3	1/10	3/10	9	9/10
4	1/10	4/10	16	16/10
5	1/10	5/10	25	25/10
6	1/10	6/10	36	36/10
7	1/10	7/10	49	49/10
8	1/10	8/10	64	64/10
9	1/10	9/10	81	81/10
Sums:		45/10	285	285/10

7.51 (a) $\mu_X = 45/10 = 4.5.$ $\sigma_X^2 = 285/10 - \mu_X^2 = 8.25.$

 (b) (i) $\mu_{\bar{X}} = 4.5.$ $\sigma_{\bar{X}}^2 = 8.25/36 = 0.23.$

  (ii) $\mu_{\bar{X}} = 4.5.$ $\sigma_{\bar{X}}^2 = 8.25/49 = 0.17.$

  (iii) $\mu_{\bar{X}} = 4.5.$ $\sigma_{\bar{X}}^2 = 8.25/100 = 0.08.$

 (c) (i) $P(4 < \bar{x} < 5) = P(\frac{4 - 4.5}{\sqrt{0.23}} < z < \frac{5 - 4.5}{\sqrt{0.23}})$

   $= P(-1.04 < z < 1.04) = 2(0.3508) = 0.7016.$

  (ii) $P(4 < \bar{x} < 5) = P(\frac{4 - 4.5}{\sqrt{0.17}} < z < \frac{5 - 4.5}{\sqrt{0.17}})$

   $= P(-1.21 < z < 1.21) = 2(0.3869) = 0.7738.$

  (iii) $P(4 < \bar{x} < 5) = P(\frac{4 - 4.5}{\sqrt{0.08}} < z < \frac{5 - 4.5}{\sqrt{0.08}})$

   $= P(-1.77 < z < 1.77) = 2(0.4616) = 0.9232.$

 (d) (i) $P(\bar{x} > 4.75) = P(z > \frac{4.75 - 4.50}{\sqrt{0.23}}) = P(z > 0.52)$

   $= 0.5 - 0.1985 = 0.3015.$

  (ii) $P(\bar{x} > 4.75) = P(z > \frac{4.75 - 4.50}{\sqrt{0.17}}) = P(z > 0.61)$

   $= 0.5 - 0.2291 = 0.2709.$

  (iii) $P(\bar{x} > 4.75) = P(z > \frac{4.75 - 4.50}{\sqrt{0.08}}) = P(z > 0.88)$

   $= 0.5 - 0.3106 = 0.1894.$

8.1 (a) $125 \pm 1.96(16/\sqrt{64})$ or $121.08 < \mu < 128.92$.

(b) $206 \pm 2.58(25/\sqrt{100})$ or $199.55 < \mu < 212.45$.

(c) $154 \pm 1.65(3/\sqrt{81})$ or $153.45 < \mu < 154.55$.

(d) $309 \pm 1.96(50/\sqrt{225})$ or $302.47 < \mu < 315.53$.

(e) $40 \pm 2.58(7/\sqrt{49})$ or $37.42 < \mu < 42.58$.

(f) $78 \pm 1.65(6/\sqrt{144})$ or $77.18 < \mu < 78.83$.

8.2 (a) $26 \pm 2.58(1.5/\sqrt{60})$ or $25.5 < \mu < 26.5$

(b) $200(0.99) = 198$.

8.3 $23.4 \pm (1.96)(7.1/\sqrt{50})$ or $21.43 < \mu < 25.37$.

8.4 $0.72 \pm 1.65(0.31/\sqrt{33})$ or $0.63 < \mu < 0.81$.

8.5 $\sum x = 2565$. $\sum x^2 = 367763$. $n = 36$.

$\bar{x} = 2565/36 = 71.25$.

$$s = \sqrt{\frac{36(367763) - (2565)^2}{36(35)}} = 72.7.$$

$71.25 \pm 1.96(72.7/\sqrt{36})$ or $47.5 < \mu < 95$.

8.6 (a) $6.30 \pm 1.28(0.9/\sqrt{100})$ or $6.18 < \mu < 6.42$.

(b) $6.30 \pm 1.96(0.9/\sqrt{100})$ or $6.12 < \mu < 6.48$.

(c) longer (80%), shorter (95%).

8.7 (a) $150 \pm 1.65(15/\sqrt{50})$ or $146.5 < \mu < 153.5$.

(b) $150 \pm 2.58(15/\sqrt{50})$ or $144.53 < \mu < 155.47$.

(c) shorter (99%), longer (90%).

8.8

Confidence Interval	10 ± 3	10 ± 4.5	10 ± 5	10 ± 8
Level of Confidence	80	90	95	99

8.9 $z(\alpha/2)(36/\sqrt{144}) = 4.95$, or $z(\alpha/2) = 1.65$.

Therefore, the level of confidence is 90%.

8.10 (a) $23.9 \pm 1.96(4.6/\sqrt{34})$ or $22.35 < \mu < 25.45$.

(b) $(1.96)(4.6/\sqrt{34}) = 1.55$.

8.11 (a) $41.8 \pm 1.96(5.7/\sqrt{33})$ or $39.86 < \mu < 43.74$.

(b) $1.96(5.7/\sqrt{33}) = 1.94$.

8.12 (a) $\bar{x} = 3500/100 = 35.$ (b) $s = \sqrt{\dfrac{100(370000) - (3500)^2}{(100)(99)}} = 50$

$$35 \pm 1.96(50/\sqrt{100}) \text{ or}$$
$$25.2 < \mu < 44.8.$$

   (c) $1.96(50/\sqrt{100}) = 9.8.$

8.13 $n = [(1.65)(1.75)/0.5]^2 = 33.35 \doteq 34.$

8.14 (a) $n = [(1.65)(20)/4]^2 = 68.06 \doteq 69.$
   (b) larger   (c) larger

8.15 (a) $n = [(1.96)(15)/5]^2 = 34.57 \doteq 35.$
   (b) smaller   (c) smaller

8.16 (a) $(18.58 + 26.42)/2 = 22.5.$ (b) $22.5 - 18.58 = 3.92.$
   (c) $1.96(30/\sqrt{n}) = 3.92$ or $\sqrt{n} = 15.$ So $n = (15)^2 = 225.$

8.17 (a) $\hat{p} = 200/400 = 0.5.$
       $0.5 \pm 1.96\sqrt{(0.5)(0.5)/400}$ or $0.451 < p < 0.549.$
   (b) $x = 0.25(900) = 225.$

       $0.25 \pm 1.65\sqrt{(0.25)(0.75)/900}$ or $0.226 < p < 0.274.$
   (c) $\hat{p} = 160/225 = 0.711.$
       $0.711 \pm 2.58\sqrt{(0.711)(0.289)/225}$ or $0.633 < p < 0.789.$
   (d) $x = 0.82(1250) = 1025.$
       $0.82 \pm 1.96\sqrt{(0.82)(0.18)/1250}$ or $0.799 < p < 0.841.$
   (e) $\hat{p} = 592/1600 = 0.37.$
       $0.37 \pm 1.65\sqrt{(0.37)(0.63)/1600}$ or $0.35 < p < 0.39.$
   (f) $x = 0.61(1000) = 610.$
       $0.61 \pm 2.58\sqrt{(0.61)(0.39)/1000}$ or $0.57 < p < 0.65.$

8.18 $\hat{p} = 105/150 = 0.7$
   $0.7 \pm 2.58\sqrt{(0.7)(0.3)/150}$ or $0.603 < p < 0.797.$

8.19 $\hat{p} = 73/90 = 0.811.$
   $0.811 \pm 1.65\sqrt{(0.811)(0.189)/90}$ or $0.743 < p < 0.879.$

8.20 (a) $\hat{p} = 26/200 = 0.13$
       $0.13 \pm 1.96\sqrt{(0.13)(0.87)/200}$ or $0.083 < p < 0.177.$

8.20 (b) $\hat{p} = 110/400 = 0.275$.

$0.275 \pm 1.96\sqrt{(0.275)(0.725)/400}$ or $0.231 < p < 0.319$.

8.21 $\hat{p} = 165/300 = 0.55$.

(a) We construct an 80% confidence interval for p.

$0.55 \pm 1.28\sqrt{(0.55)(0.45)/300}$ or $0.513 < p < 0.587$.

Yes. The confidence interval does not contain 0.5.

(b) We construct a 98% confidence interval for p.

$0.55 \pm 2.33\sqrt{(0.55)(0.45)/300}$ or $0.483 < p < 0.617$.

No. The confidence interval contains 0.5.

(c) (i) Yes. (ii) No.

8.22 (a) $\hat{p} = 112/200 = 0.56$.

(b) $0.56 \pm 1.65\sqrt{(0.56)(0.44)/200}$ or $0.502 < p < 0.618$.

(c) $1.65\sqrt{(0.56)(0.44)/200} = 0.058$

8.23 (a) $\hat{p} = 45/75 = 0.6$.

(b) $0.6 \pm 1.96\sqrt{(0.6)(0.4)/75}$ or $0.489 < p < 0.711$.

(c) $1.96\sqrt{(0.6)(0.4)/75} = 0.111$.

8.24 (a) $0.82 \pm 1.96\sqrt{(0.82)(0.18)/75}$ or $0.733 < p < 0.907$.

(b) $1.96\sqrt{(0.82)(0.18)/75} = 0.087$.

8.25 $n = (1.65/0.03)^2(1/4) = 756.25 \doteq 757$.

8.26 $n = (1.96/0.04)^2(1/4) = 600.25 \doteq 601$.

8.27 (a) $n = (1.65/0.02)^2(1/4) = 1701.56 \doteq 1702$.

(b) $n = (2.58/0.02)^2(1/4) = 4160.25 \doteq 4161$.

8.28 (a) (i) larger (ii) smaller

$n = (1.96/0.02)^2(1/4) = 2401$

(b) larger $n = (1.65/0.01)^2(1/4) = 6806.25 \doteq 6807$.

(c) smaller $n = (1.65/0.04)^2(1/4) = 425.39 \doteq 426$.

8.29 (a) (i) H_0: $\mu \le 72$. H_a: $\mu > 72$. (ii) right-tail.

(iii) type I: The true mean amount of rainfall of at most 72 inches is rejected.
type II: The false mean amount of rainfall of at most 72 inches is not rejected.

118

8.29 (b) (i) H_0: $\mu = 250$ H_a: $\mu \neq 250$

(ii) two-tail

(iii) type I: The true mean amount of 250 borrowed books is rejected.
type II: The false mean amount of 250 borrowed books is not rejected.

(c) (i) H_0: $\mu \geq 78$ H_a: $\mu < 78$

(ii) left-tail

(iii) type I: The true mean temperature of at least 78° is rejected.
type II: The false mean temperature of at least 78° is not rejected.

(d) (i) H_0: $\mu \leq 36$ H_a: $\mu > 36$

(ii) right-tail

(iii) type I: The true mean age of professors of at most 36 years is rejected.
type II: The false mean age of professors of at most 36 years is not rejected.

(e) (i) H_0: $\mu \geq 19500$ H_a: $\mu < 19500$

(ii) left-tail

(iii) type I: The true mean salary of at least $19500 is rejected.
type II: The false mean salary of at least $19500 is not rejected.

(f) (i) H_0: $\mu = 18000$ H_a: $\mu \neq 18000$

(ii) two-tail

(iii) type I: The true mean number of 18000 families is rejected. type II: The false mean number of 18000 families is not rejected.

(g) (i) H_0: $\mu \leq 2.3$ H_a: $\mu > 2.3$

(ii) right-tail

(iii) type I: The true mean grade-point average of at most 2.3 is rejected. type II: The false mean grade-point average of at most 2.3 is not rejected.

8.30 (a) $H_0: \mu \le 90$ $H_a: \mu > 90$

    (b) (i) $z \ge 2.33$ (ii) $z \ge 1.65$ (iii) $z \ge 1.28$

8.31 (a) $H_0: \mu = 90$ $H_a: \mu \ne 90$

    (b) (i) $z \le -2.58$ or $z \ge 2.58$

        (ii) $z \le -1.96$ or $z \ge 1.96$

          (iii) $z \le -1.65$ or $z \ge 1.65$

8.32 (a) $H_0: \mu \ge 90$ $H_a: \mu < 90$

    (b) (i) $z \le -2.33$ (ii) $z \le -1.65$ (iii) $z \le -1.28$

8.33 $H_0: \mu \ge 30$ $H_a: \mu < 30$

The critical regions are: (i) $z \le -2.33$ (ii) $z \le -1.65$

(iii) $z \le -1.28$

(a) $z = \dfrac{24 - 30}{40/\sqrt{100}} = -1.5$

    (i) fail to reject H_0 (ii) fail to reject H_0

    (iii) reject H_0

(b) $z = \dfrac{24 - 30}{40/\sqrt{400}} = -3$

    (i) reject H_0 (ii) reject H_0 (iii) reject H_0

(c) $z = \dfrac{24 - 30}{20/\sqrt{100}} = -3$

    (i) reject H_0 (ii) reject H_0 (iii) reject H_0

8.34 $H_0: \mu \le 30$ $H_a: \mu > 30$

(a) $\alpha = P(\bar{x} \ge 30) = P(z \ge \dfrac{30 - 30}{40/\sqrt{64}}) = P(z \ge 0) = 0.5$

(b) $\alpha = P(\bar{x} \ge 32) = P(z \ge \dfrac{32 - 30}{40/\sqrt{64}}) = P(z \ge 0.4)$

    $= 0.5 - 0.1554 = 0.3446$

8.34 (c) $\alpha = P(\overline{x} \geq 38) = P(z \geq \dfrac{38 - 30}{40/\sqrt{64}}) = P(z \geq 1.6)$

$= 0.5 - 0.4452 = 0.0548$

(d) $\alpha = P(\overline{x} \geq 40) = P(z \geq \dfrac{40 - 30}{40/\sqrt{64}}) = P(z \geq 2)$

$= 0.5 - 0.4772 = 0.0228$

8.35 $H_0: \mu \leq 150$ $H_a: \mu > 150$ $\alpha = 0.05$

Observed value: $z = \dfrac{153-150}{7.5/\sqrt{40}} = 2.53$

Critical value: $z = 1.65$. Decision: reject H_0. The data suggest that the mean time is more than 150 minutes. type I: The true mean time of at most 150 minutes is rejected.

8.36 $H_0: \mu \geq 60$ $H_a: \mu < 60$ $\alpha = 0.05$

Observed value: $z = \dfrac{58.5-60}{5/\sqrt{50}} = -2.12$

Critical value: $z = -1.65$. Decision: reject H_0. The data indicate that the handballs are not bouncing according to specification. type I: A true mean bounce of at least 60 inches is rejected.

8.37 $H_0: \mu \leq 385$ $H_a: \mu > 385$ $\alpha = 0.05$

Observed value: $z = \dfrac{395 - 385}{26/\sqrt{35}} = 2.28$

Critical value: $z = 1.65$. Decision: reject H_0. The data indicate that there has been an increase in the number of books loaned out.

8.38 $H_0: \mu \leq 27$ $H_a: \mu > 27$ $\alpha = 0.05$

Observed value: $z = \dfrac{30-27}{6/\sqrt{40}} = 3.16$. Critical value: $z = 1.65$

Decision: reject H_0. There is sufficient evidence indicating the mean breaking strength has increased.

8.39 H_0: $\mu \leq 27$ H_a: $\mu > 27$ $\alpha = 0.05$

Observed value: $z = \dfrac{30 - 27}{15/\sqrt{40}} = 1.26$.

Critical value: $z = 1.65$. Decision: fail to reject H_0.
A smaller standard deviation improves the likelihood of
rejecting a false hypothesis.

8.40 (a) H_0: $\mu = 700$ H_a: $\mu \neq 700$ $\alpha = 0.05$

Observed value: $z = \dfrac{675 - 700}{77/\sqrt{48}} = -2.25$

Critical values: $z = \pm 1.96$. Decision: reject H_0.
The data do not support the manufacturer's claim
that the mops last a mean time of 700 hours.

(b) type I   (c)   0.05

8.41 (a) H_0: $\mu \geq 16$ H_a: $\mu < 16$ $\alpha = 0.01$

Observed value: $z = \dfrac{15.1-16}{3/\sqrt{100}} = -3$

Critical value: $z = -2.33$. Decision: reject H_0.
The data indicate that the mean content is less
than 16 ounces.

(b) Since $P(z \leq -3) = 0.5 - 0.4987 = 0.0013$, the probability of observing a value as or more extreme than the
observed value is very small (provided H_0 is true).

(c) yes   (d) $10{,}000(0.0013) = 13$ (e)   yes

8.42 (a) $P(\bar{x} \geq 35) = P(z > \dfrac{35 - 30}{40/\sqrt{64}}) = P(z \geq 1) = 0.5 - 0.3413 = 0.1587$

(b) $P(\bar{x} \geq 37) = P(z > \dfrac{37 - 30}{40/\sqrt{64}}) = P(z \geq 1.4) = 0.5-0.4192 = 0.0808$

(c) $P(\bar{x} \geq 39) = P(z > \dfrac{39 - 30}{40/\sqrt{64}}) = P(z \geq 1.8) = 0.5-0.4641 = 0.0359$

(d) $2(0.1587) = 0.3174$ $2(0.0808) = 0.1616$

$2(0.0359) = 0.0718$

8.43   (a) $P(\bar{x} \geq 35) = P(z \geq \dfrac{35 - 30}{40/\sqrt{100}}) = P(z \geq 1.25)$

$$= 0.5 - 0.3944 = 0.1056$$

    (b) $P(\bar{x} \geq 37) = P(z \geq \dfrac{37 - 30}{40/\sqrt{100}}) = P(z \geq 1.75)$

$$= 0.5 - 0.4599 = 0.0401$$

    (c) $P(\bar{x} \geq 39) = P(z \geq \dfrac{39 - 30}{40/\sqrt{100}}) = P(z \geq 2.25)$

$$= 0.5 - 0.4878 = 0.0122$$

    (d) $2(0.1056) = 0.2112$ $2(0.0401) = 0.0802$
             $2(0.0122) = 0.0244$

8.44 $H_0: \mu \geq 12$ $H_a: \mu < 12$

    (a) $P(\bar{x} \leq 11.25) = P(z \leq \dfrac{11.25 - 12}{3/\sqrt{36}}) = P(z \leq -1.50)$

$$= 0.5 - 0.4332 = 0.0668$$

    (b)   (i)   yes   (ii)   no   (iii)   no

    (c)   (i)   type I   (ii)   type II   (iii)   type II

8.45 $H_0: \mu = 6$ $H_a: \mu \neq 6$

    (a) $P\text{-value} = 2P(\bar{x} \leq 5.95) = 2P(z \leq \dfrac{5.95-6}{0.15/\sqrt{40}}) = 2P(z \leq -2.11)$

$$= 2(0.5 - 0.4826) = 2(0.0174) = 0.0348$$

    (b)   (i)   yes   (ii)   yes   (iii)   no

    (c)   (i)   type I   (ii)   type I   (iii)   type II

8.46 $H_0: \mu = 30$ $H_a: \mu \neq 30$

    (a) $P\text{-value} = 2P(\bar{x} \geq 30.1) = 2P(z \geq \dfrac{30.1 - 30}{0.25/\sqrt{50}}) = 2P(z \geq 2.83)$

$$= 2(0.5 - 0.4977) = 2(0.0023) = 0.0046$$

    (b)   (i)   yes   (ii)   yes   (iii)   yes

    (c)   (i)   type I   (ii)   type I   (iii) type I

8.47   Any level of significance larger than or equal to 0.07.

8.48 (a) (i) H_0: p =0.53 H_a: p ≠ 0.53   (ii) two-tail

(iii) type I: The true proportion 0.53 of voters who favor the death penalty is rejected.

type II: The false proportion 0.53 of voters who favor the death penalty is not rejected.

(b) (i) H_0: p ≥ 0.06 H_a: p < 0.06   (ii) left-tail

(iii) type I: The true proportion of at least 0.06 of a product that breaks down before the guarantee expires is rejected.

type II: The false proportion of at least 0.06 of a product that breaks down before the guarantee expires is rejected.

(c) (i) H_0: p ≥ 0.90 H_a: p < 0.90   (ii) left-tail

(iii) type I: The true proportion of at least 0.90 of full-time college students younger than 23 years of age is rejected.

type II: The false proportion of at least 0.90 of full-time college students younger than 23 years of age is not rejected.

(d) (i) H_0: p ≤ 0.07 H_a: p > 0.07   (ii) right-tail

(iii) type I: The true proportion of at most 0.07 of minority students enrolled at a large university is rejected.

type II: The false proportion of at most 0.07 of minority students enrolled at a large university is not rejected.

(e) (i) H_0: p = 0.40 H_a: p ≠ 0.40   (ii) two-tail

(iii) type I: The true proportion 0.40 of persons surviving a certain cancer for 5 years is rejected.

type II: The false proportion 0.40 of persons surviving a certain cancer for 5 years is not rejected.

(f) (i) H_0: p ≥ 0.05 H_a: p < 0.05   (ii) left-tail

(iii) type I: The true proportion of at least 0.05 of defective items is rejected.

type II: The false proportion of at least 0.05 of defective items is not rejected.

8.48 (g) (i) H_0: $p \leq 0.30$ H_a: $p > 0.30$ (ii) right-tail

(iii) type I: The true proportion of at most 0.30 of high school graduates seeking full-time employment is rejected.

type II: The false proportion of at most 0.30 of high school graduates seeking full-time employment is not rejected.

8.49 (a) H_0: $p \geq 0.80$ H_a: $p \leq 0.80$

(i) $z \leq -1.28$ (ii) $z \leq -1.65$ (iii) $z \leq -2.33$

(b) H_0: $p = 0.80$ H_a: $p \neq 0.80$

(i) $z \leq -1.65$ or $z \geq 1.65$ (ii) $z \leq -1.96$ or $z \geq 1.96$

(iii) $z \leq -2.58$ or $z \geq 2.58$

(c) H_0: $p \leq 0.80$ H_a: $p \geq 0.80$

(i) $z \geq 1.28$ (ii) $z \geq 1.65$ (iii) $z \geq 2.33$

8.50 H_0: $p \geq 0.70$ H_a: $p < 0.70$

(a) (i) $z \leq -1.28$

(ii) Observed value: $z = \dfrac{65 - (100)(0.7)}{\sqrt{(100)(0.7)(0.3)}} = -1.09$

Decision: fail to reject H_0 (iii) type II

(b) (i) $z \leq -1.65$

(ii) Observed value: $z = \dfrac{60 - (100)(0.7)}{\sqrt{(100)(0.7)(0.3)}} = -2.18$

Decision: reject H_0 (iii) type I

(c) (i) $z \leq -2.33$

(ii) Observed value: $z = \dfrac{260 - (400)(0.7)}{\sqrt{(400)(0.7)(0.3)}} = -2.18$

Decision: fail to reject H_0 (iii) type II

(d) (i) $z \leq -2.33$

(ii) Observed value: $z = \dfrac{1040 - (1600)(0.7)}{\sqrt{(1600)(0.7)(0.3)}} = -4.36$

Decision: reject H_0 (iii) type I

8.51 H_0: $p \leq 0.50$ H_a: $p > 0.50$ $\alpha = 0.10$

Observed value: $z = \dfrac{105-(200)(0.5)}{\sqrt{(200)(0.5)(0.5)}} = 0.71$

Critical value: $z = 1.28$. Decision: fail to reject H_0.
The data do not support the politician's claim.

8.52 H_0: $p \leq 0.20$ H_a: $p > 0.20$ $\alpha = 0.01$

Observed value: $z = \dfrac{63 - (225)(0.2)}{\sqrt{(225)(0.2)(0.8)}} = 3$

P-value = $P(z \geq 3) = 0.5 - 0.4987 = 0.0013$. Reject H_0.
The data indicate that more than 20% did not receive
diplomas.

8.53 H_0: $p \leq 0.05$ H_a: $p > 0.05$ $\alpha = 0.05$

Observed value: $z = \dfrac{14 - (160)(0.05)}{\sqrt{(160)(0.05)(0.95)}} = 2.18$

Critical value: $z = 1.65$. Decision: reject H_0. The
retailer does not accept the shipment.

8.54 (a) H_0: $p = 0.20$ H_a: $p \neq 0.20$ $\alpha = 0.05$

Observed value: $z = \dfrac{11 - (40)(0.2)}{\sqrt{(40)(0.2)(0.8)}} = 1.19$

Critical values: $z = \pm 1.96$. Decision: fail to
reject H_0. The data do not support rejecting the
claim.

(b) type II

8.55 (a) H_0: $p \leq 0.52$ H_a: $p > 0.52$ $\alpha = 0.05$

Observed value: $z = \dfrac{57 - (100)(0.52)}{\sqrt{(100)(0.52)(0.48)}} = 1$

Critical value: $z = 1.65$. Decision: fail to reject
H_0. The data do not indicate that she has gained
support.

(b) Observed value: $z = \dfrac{228 - (400)(0.52)}{\sqrt{(400)(0.52)(0.48)}} = 2$

Critical value: $z = 1.65$. Decision: reject H_0.
The data support the politician's claim that she has

8.55   (b)   (Continued)
       gained support.

       (c)   A larger sample size increases the likelihood of
             rejecting a false hypothesis.

8.56   Use α = 0.01.   It would be costly to market the new pill.
       If the new pill were no more effective than the old pill,
       the company would have to absorb the cost of marketing
       the new pill.   With α = 0.01, rejection of the null
       hypothesis would provide strong evidence that the new pill
       is more effective.

8.57 $100(0.95) = 95$; $1000(0.99) = 990$.

8.58 $210 \pm 1.96(6/\sqrt{60})$ or $208.48 < \mu < 211.52$.

8.59   (a) $38622 \pm 1.96(44506/\sqrt{36})$ or $24083 < \mu < 53161$

       (b) $45308 \pm 1.96(52535/\sqrt{36})$ or $28147 < \mu < 62469$

       (c) $41965 \pm 1.96(48686/\sqrt{72})$ or $30719 < \mu < 53211$

8.60 $\bar{x} = 19942/40 = 498.55$

       $s = \sqrt{\dfrac{40(10276986) - (19942)^2}{(40)(39)}} = 92.67$

       $498.55 \pm 1.96(92.67/\sqrt{40})$ or $469.83 < \mu < 527.27$

8.61 $\bar{x} = 2284/32 = 71.38$

       $s = \sqrt{\dfrac{32(163232) - (2284)^2}{(32)(31)}} = 2.61$

       $71.38 \pm (2.58)(2.61/\sqrt{32})$ or $70.19 < \mu < 72.57$

8.62   (a) $(14170 + 14830)/2 = 14500$

       (b) $z(\alpha/2)(3000/\sqrt{225}) = 14500 - 14170 = 330$, or $z(\alpha/2) = 1.65$.
             Therefore, the level of confidence is 90%.

8.63 $(2.33)(s/\sqrt{225}) = (15989.30 - 15010.70)/2 = 489.3$.
       Therefore $s = (489.3)\sqrt{225}/2.33 = 3150$.

8.64 $(2.33)(3570/\sqrt{n}) = (15489.30 - 14510.70)/2 = 489.3$.
       Therefore, $\sqrt{n} = (2.33)(3570)/489.3 = 17$, or $n = 289$.

8.65 $n = [(1.96)(17)/2]^2 = 277.56 \doteq 278$

8.66 $n = [(2.33)(3)/0.5]^2 = 195.44 \doteq 196$

8.67 $n = [(1.65)(10)/2]^2 = 68.06 \doteq 69$

$n = [(2.58)(10)/2]^2 = 166.41 \doteq 167$

8.68 (a) (i) larger (ii) smaller

(b) $n = [(1.96)(10)/2]^2 = 96.04 \doteq 97$

8.69 (a) larger (b) $n = [(1.65)(10)/1]^2 = 272.25 \doteq 273$

8.70 (a) 147 (b) $147 \pm 1.96(20/\sqrt{70})$ or $142.31 < \mu < 151.69$

(c) $1.96(20/\sqrt{70}) = 4.69$

8.71 (a) $x = 0.5(100) = 50$

$0.5 \pm 1.96\sqrt{(0.5)(0.5)/100}$ or $0.402 < p < 0.598$

(b) $\hat{p} = 50/125 = 0.4$

$0.4 \pm 1.65\sqrt{(0.4)(0.6)/125}$ or $0.328 < p < 0.472$

(c) $x = 0.72(400) = 288$

$0.72 \pm 2.58\sqrt{(0.72)(0.28)/400}$ or $0.662 < p < 0.778$

(d) $\hat{p} = 45/225 = 0.2$

$0.2 \pm 1.96\sqrt{(0.2)(0.8)/225}$ or $0.148 < p < 0.252$

(e) $x = 0.64(60) = 38$

$0.64 \pm 1.65\sqrt{(0.64)(0.36)/60}$ or $0.538 < p < 0.742$

(f) $\hat{p} = 30/50 = 0.6$

$0.6 \pm 2.58\sqrt{(0.6)(0.4)/50}$ or $0.421 < p < 0.779$

8.72 $\hat{p} = 96/110 = 0.873$

$0.873 \pm 2.58\sqrt{(0.873)(0.127)/110}$ or $0.791 < p < 0.955$

8.73 (a) $\hat{p} = 126/300 = 0.42$

$0.42 \pm 1.65\sqrt{(0.42)(0.58)/300}$ or $0.373 < p < 0.467$

(b) $1.65\sqrt{(0.42)(0.58)/300} = 0.047$

8.74 (a) $\hat{p} = 306/450 = 0.68$

$0.68 \pm 1.96\sqrt{(0.68)(0.32)/450}$ or $0.637 < p < 0.723$

(b) $1.96\sqrt{(0.68)(0.32)/450} = 0.043$

8.75 (a) $n = (1.96/0.04)^2 (1/4) = 600.25 \doteq 601$

(b) $n = (1.96/0.02)^2 (1/4) = 2401$

(c) $n = (1.96/0.01)^2 (1/4) = 9604$

8.76 (a) $H_0: \mu \leq 400$ $H_a: \mu > 400$ $\alpha = 0.05$

Observed value: $z = \dfrac{407 - 400}{40/\sqrt{64}} = 1.4$

Critical value: $z = 1.65$. Decision: fail to reject H_0. The data do not support the claim that more than 400 books are loaned out per day, on average.

(b) type II.

8.77 $H_0: \mu \geq 25$ $H_a: \mu < 25$ $\alpha = 0.10$

Observed value: $z = \dfrac{23.4 - 25}{7.1/\sqrt{50}} = -1.59$

Critical value: $z = -1.28$. Decision: reject H_0. The data indicate that the mean waiting time is less than 25 minutes.

8.78 $H_0: \mu = 450$ $H_a: \mu \neq 450$ $\alpha = 0.01$

Observed value: $z = \dfrac{450.4 - 450}{0.95/\sqrt{43}} = 2.76$

Critical values: $z = \pm 2.58$. Decision: reject H_0. The data do not support the manufacturer's claim.

8.79 $H_0: \mu \leq 3.25$ $H_a: \mu > 3.25$ $\alpha = 0.05$

Observed value: $z = \dfrac{3.35 - 3.25}{0.40/\sqrt{31}} = 1.39$

Critical value: $z = 1.65$. Decision: fail to reject H_0. There is insufficient evidence to conclude that the length is more than 3.25 inches.

8.80 $H_0: \mu \geq 12$ $H_a: \mu < 12$ $\alpha = 0.05$

Observed value: $z = \dfrac{11.85 - 12}{0.65/\sqrt{38}} = -1.42$

Critical value: $z = -1.65$. Decision: fail to reject H_0. There is insufficient evidence to conclude the mean length is less than 12 inches.

8.81 H_0: $\mu \leq 36.2$ H_a: $\mu > 36.2$ $\alpha = 0.05$

Observed value: $z = \dfrac{41.8-36.2}{5.7/\sqrt{33}} = 5.64$

Critical value: $z = 1.65$. Decision: reject H_0. The data support the nutritionist's claim.

8.82 H_0: $\mu \leq 500$ H_a: $\mu > 500$

(a) P-value $= P(\overline{x} \geq 504) = P(z \geq \dfrac{504-500}{20/\sqrt{100}}) = P(z \geq 2)$

$= 0.5 - 0.4772 = 0.0228$

(b) yes (at the 10% level of significance).

no (at the 1% level of significance).

8.83 H_0: $\mu \geq 15$ H_a: $\mu \leq 15$

(a) P-value $= P(\overline{x} \leq 14) = P(z < \dfrac{14-15}{2/\sqrt{36}}) = P(z \leq -3)$

$= 0.5 - 0.4987 = 0.0013$

(b) reject H_0 in both cases.

8.84 $\hat{p} = 15/50 = 0.3$

H_0: $p \leq 0.2$ H_a: $p > 0.2$ $\alpha = 0.05$

Observed value: $z = \dfrac{15 - (50)(0.2)}{\sqrt{(50)(0.2)(0.8)}} = 1.77$

Critical value: $z = 1.65$. Decision: reject H_0. The data indicate that more than 20% of the unpaid bills are overdue.

8.85 H_0: $p \geq 0.1$ H_a: $p \leq 0.1$

Observed value: $z = \dfrac{4-(100)(0.1)}{\sqrt{(100)(0.1)(0.9)}} = -2$

Critical value: $z = -2.33$ ($\alpha = 0.01$)
$z = -1.28$ ($\alpha = 0.10$)

Decision: fail to reject H_0 ($\alpha = 0.01$)
reject H_0 ($\alpha = 0.10$)

8.86 $\hat{p} = 29/60 = 0.483$

$H_0: p = 0.5$ $\qquad$ $H_a: p \neq 0.5$ $\qquad$ $\alpha = 0.10$

Observed value: $z = \dfrac{29 - (60)(0.5)}{\sqrt{(60)(0.5)(0.5)}} = -0.26$

Critical values: $z = \pm 1.65$. Decision: fail to reject H_0. There is not sufficient evidence to reject the null hypothesis.

8.87 (a) $z = \dfrac{\bar{x} - 150}{20/\sqrt{100}} < -1.65$ or $\bar{x} < 150 - (1.65)2 = 146.7$.

Therefore, the critical region is $z < -1.65$ or $\bar{x} < 146.7$.

$\beta = P(\bar{x} > 146.7 \mid \mu = 146) = P(z > \dfrac{146.7 - 146}{20/\sqrt{100}}) = P(z > 0.35)$

$= 0.5 - 0.1368 = 0.3632$.

(b) $z = \dfrac{\bar{x} - 150}{20/\sqrt{100}} < -1.28$ or $\bar{x} < 150 - (1.28)2 = 147.44$.

Therefore, the critical region is $z < -1.28$ or $\bar{x} < 147.44$.

$\beta = P(\bar{x} > 147.44 \mid \mu = 146) = P(z > \dfrac{147.44 - 146}{20/\sqrt{100}})$

$= P(z > 0.72) = 0.5 - 0.2642 = 0.2358$.

(c) α increases (decreases) if and only if β decreases (increases), assuming the same sample size.

(d) $z = \dfrac{\bar{x} - 150}{20/\sqrt{100}} < -2.33$ or $\bar{x} < 150 - (2.33)(2) = 145.34$.

Therefore, the critical region is $z < -2.33$ or $\bar{x} < 145.34$.

$\beta = P(\bar{x} > 145.34 \mid \mu = 146) = P(z > \dfrac{145.34 - 146}{20/\sqrt{100}})$

$= P(z > -0.33) = 0.5 + 0.1293 = 0.6293$.

(e) $z = \dfrac{\bar{x} - 150}{20/\sqrt{400}} < -2.33$ or $\bar{x} < 150 - (2.33)(1) = 147.67$.

Therefore, the critical region is $z < -2.33$ or $\bar{x} < 147.67$.

$\beta = P(\bar{x} > 147.67 \mid \mu = 146) = P(z > \dfrac{147.67 - 146}{20/\sqrt{400}}) = P(z > 1.67)$

8.87 (e) (Continued)

$$= 0.5 - 0.4525 = 0.0475.$$

(f) The sample size increases (decreases) if and only if β decreases (increases), assuming the same level of significance.

8.88

p = 0.4			p = 0.7	
x	P(x)		x	P(x)
0	0.078		0	0.002
1	0.259		1	0.028
2	0.346		2	0.132
3	0.230		3	0.309
4	0.077		4	0.360
5	0.010		5	0.168

(a) $\alpha = 0.077 + 0.010 = 0.087$

(b) $\beta = 0.002 + 0.028 + 0.132 + 0.309 = 0.471$

8.89 (a) larger. $\alpha = 0.230 + 0.077 + 0.010 = 0.317$

(b) smaller. $\beta = 0.002 + 0.028 + 0.132 = 0.162$

8.90 $\bar{x} = \sum x/n = 1767/32 = 55.22$

$$s = \sqrt{\frac{n(\sum x^2) - (\sum x)^2}{n(n-1)}} = \sqrt{\frac{(32)(98755) - (1767)^2}{(32)(31)}} = 6.18$$

$H_0: \mu \geq 60$ $\qquad$ $H_a: \mu < 60$ $\qquad$ $\alpha = 0.05$

Observed value: $z = \dfrac{55.22 - 60}{6.18/\sqrt{32}} = -4.38$

Critical value: $z = -1.65$. Decision: reject H_0. The data suggest that the mean down time per week is less than 60 minutes.

8.91 $\bar{x} = \sum x/n = 170.9/35 = 4.883$

$$s = \sqrt{\frac{n(\sum x^2) - (\sum x)^2}{n(n-1)}} = \sqrt{\frac{(35)(836.75) - (170.9)^2}{(35)(34)}} = 0.258$$

$H_0: \mu = 5$ $\qquad$ $H_a: \mu \neq 5$ $\qquad$ $\alpha = 0.01$

Observed value: $z = \dfrac{4.883 - 5}{0.258/\sqrt{35}} = -2.68$

Critical values: $z = \pm 2.58$. Decision: reject H_0. The data do not support the manufacturer's claim.

9.1

	t(0.005)	t(0.01)	t(0.025)	t(0.05)	t(0.10)
(a)	3.707	3.143	2.447	1.943	1.440
(b)	3.055	2.681	2.179	1.782	1.356
(c)	2.787	2.485	2.060	1.708	1.316

9.2 (a) 9 (b) 0.01 (c) 1.323 (d) 8

(e) 0.005 (f) 4.604 (g) 17 (h) 0.10

(i) 5.841 (j) 19 (k) 0.025 (ℓ) 1.734

9.3 (a) (i) H_0: $\mu \leq 16$ H_a: $\mu > 16$ $\alpha = 0.10$

Observed value: $t = \dfrac{18-16}{4/\sqrt{14}} = 1.87$,   df = 13

Critical value: t = 1.35. Decision: reject H_0.
(ii) type I.

(b) (i) H_0: $\mu \geq 27$ H_a: $\mu < 27$ $\alpha = 0.05$

Observed value: $t = \dfrac{23-27}{7/\sqrt{9}} = -1.71$,   df = 8

Critical value: t = -1.86. Decision: fail to
reject H_0.

(ii) type II

(c) (i) H_0: $\mu = 30$ H_a: $\mu \neq 30$ $\alpha = 0.01$

Observed value: $t = \dfrac{25 - 30}{4/\sqrt{6}} = -3.06$,   df = 5

Critical values: t = $\pm$4.032. Decision: fail to
reject H_0.

(ii) type II

(d) (i) H_0: $\mu \leq 125$ H_a: $\mu > 125$ $\alpha = 0.05$

Observed value: $t = \dfrac{128 - 125}{18/\sqrt{40}} = 1.05$,   df = 39 (large)

Critical value: t = 1.645. Decision: fail to
reject H_0.

(ii) type II

9.3 (e) (i) $H_0: \mu \geq 50$ $H_a: \mu < 50$ $\alpha = 0.025$

Observed value: $t = \dfrac{45 - 50}{10/\sqrt{20}} = -2.24$, df = 19

Critical value: $t = -2.093$. Decision: reject H_0.
  (ii) type I

(f) (i) $H_0: \mu = 60$ $H_a: \mu \neq 60$ $\alpha = 0.10$

Observed value: $t = \dfrac{70 - 60}{16/\sqrt{8}} = 1.77$, df = 7.

Critical values: $t = \pm 1.895$. Decision: fail to reject H_0

  (ii) type II

9.4 Table B-4 is used in parts (a)-(f) below.
  (a) $0.025 < \text{P-value} = P(t \geq 1.87) < 0.05$ with df = 13.
      For $\alpha = 0.10$, reject H_0.
  (b) $0.05 < \text{P-value} = P(t \leq -1.71) < 0.10$ with df = 8.
      For $\alpha = 0.05$, fail to reject H_0.
  (c) $0.01 < P(t \leq -3.06) < 0.025$ with df = 5.
      So $2(0.01) = 0.02 < 2P(t \leq -3.06) = \text{P-value} < 2(0.025)$
      $= 0.05$.
      For $\alpha = 0.01$, fail to reject H_0.
  (d) $0.10 < \text{P-value} = P(t \geq 1.05) < 0.25$ with df = 39 (large).
      For $\alpha = 0.05$, fail to reject H_0.
  (e) $0.01 < \text{P-value} = P(t \leq -2.24) < 0.025$ with df = 19.
      For $\alpha = 0.025$, reject H_0.
  (f) $0.05 < P(t \geq 1.77) < 0.10$ with df = 7. So
      $2(0.05) = 0.10 < 2P(t \geq 1.77) = \text{P-value} < 2(0.10) = 0.20$.
      For $\alpha = 0.10$, fail to reject H_0.

9.5　H_0: $\mu \leq 23750$　　　　　H_a: $\mu > 23750$

Observed value:　$t = \dfrac{24100 - 23750}{420/\sqrt{9}} = 2.5$,　$df = 8$.

Critical value:　$t = 1.86(\alpha = 0.05)$
　　　　　　　　$t = 2.896(\alpha = 0.01)$

Decision:　reject H_0 ($\alpha = 0.05$); fail to reject H_0 ($\alpha = 0.01$)

9.6　H_0: $\mu \geq 22$　　　　H_a: $\mu < 22$　　　　$\alpha = 0.01$

Observed value:　$t = \dfrac{20.5 - 22}{(2.5)/\sqrt{24}} = -2.94$,　$df = 23$

Critical value:　$t = -2.5$.　Decision:　reject H_0.　The data suggest that the mean release time is less than 22 months.

9.7　H_0: $\mu \geq 160$　　　　H_a: $\mu < 160$

Observed value:　$t = \dfrac{148 - 160}{9.5/\sqrt{8}} = -3.57$,　$df = 7$.

P-value $= P(t \leq -3.57) < 0.005$.
The null hypothesis would be rejected for any $\alpha \geq 0.005$.

9.8　H_0: $\mu \leq 30$　　　　H_a: $\mu > 30$　　　　$\alpha = 0.01$

Observed value:　$t = \dfrac{34 - 30}{6/\sqrt{25}} = 3.33$,　$df = 24$.

Critical value:　$t = 2.492$.　Decision: reject H_0.　The data indicate that the mean amount spent per customer is more than $30.

9.9　H_0: $\mu = 6000$　　　　H_a: $\mu \neq 6000$　　　　$\alpha = 0.05$

Observed value:　$t = \dfrac{6200 - 6000}{300/\sqrt{20}} = 2.98$,　$df = 19$.

Critical values:　$t = \pm 2.093$.　Decision: reject H_0.　The data do not support the claim that the mean contribution per family is $6000.

9.10 $H_0: \mu \leq 10$ $H_a: \mu > 10$

Observed value: $t = \dfrac{12 - 10}{5/\sqrt{18}} = 1.7$,   df = 17.

$0.05 < \text{P-value} = P(t \geq 1.70) < 0.10$.

We can determine from this the following:

$\alpha \geq 0.10$, reject H_0; $\alpha \leq 0.05$, fail to reject H_0.

9.11 $\bar{x} = \sum x/n = 160.7/12 = 13.392$

$s = \sqrt{\dfrac{n(\sum x^2) - (\sum x)^2}{n(n-1)}} = \sqrt{\dfrac{12(2165.29) - (13.392)^2}{(12)(11)}} = 1.097$

$H_0: \mu \leq 13$ $H_a: \mu > 13$ $\alpha = 0.05$

Observed value: $t = \dfrac{13.392 - 13}{1.097/\sqrt{12}} = 1.24$,   df = 11.

Critical value: $t = 1.796$. Decision: fail to reject H_0. There is insufficient evidence to conclude that the mean time to repair is more than 13 months.

9.12 $H_0: \mu \geq 36.2$ $H_a: \mu < 36.2$ $\alpha = 0.05$

Observed value: $t = \dfrac{28.7 - 36.2}{5.7/\sqrt{28}} = -6.96$,   df = 27.

Critical value: $t = -1.703$. Decision: reject H_0. There is sufficient evidence to suggest that the mean percent calories from fat is less than 36.2.

9.13 (a) $28.7 \pm (2.052)(5.7/\sqrt{28})$ or $26.49 < \mu < 30.91$.
      (b) Yes. The confidence interval does not contain 36.2.
      (c) $(2.052)(5.7/\sqrt{28}) = 2.21$.

9.14 (a) $65.8 \pm 2.201(1.95/\sqrt{12})$ or $64.56 < \mu < 67.04$.
      (b) $(2.201)(1.95/\sqrt{12}) = 1.24$.

9.15 $13.392 \pm 1.796(1.097/\sqrt{12})$ or $12.823 < \mu < 13.961$.

9.16

	$\chi^2(0.01)$	$\chi^2(0.025)$	$\chi^2(0.05)$	$\chi^2(0.95)$	$\chi^2(0.99)$
(a)	20.090	17.535	15.507	2.733	1.646
(b)	30.578	27.488	24.996	7.261	5.229
(c)	44.314	40.646	37.652	14.611	11.524

9.17 (a) 16.812 (b) 0.872 (c) 12.592 (d) 10.645
  (e) 0.872 (f) 1.635

9.18 (a) 11 (b) 0.95 (c) 3.94 (d) 25 (e) 0.10
  (f) 27.587 (g) 12.443 (h) 3.053

9.19 (a) (i) H_0: $\sigma^2 \leq 100$ H_a: $\sigma^2 > 100$ $\alpha = 0.05$

Observed value: $\chi^2 = \dfrac{(16-1)(173)}{100} = 25.95$, df = 15.

Critical value: $\chi^2 = 24.996$. Decision: reject H_0.
  (ii) type I.

  (b) (i) H_0: $\sigma^2 \geq 70$ H_a: $\sigma^2 < 70$ $\alpha = 0.01$

Observed value: $\chi^2 = \dfrac{(12-1)(12.7)}{70} = 2$, df = 11.

Critical value: $\chi^2 = 3.053$. Decision: reject H_0.
  (ii) type I.

  (c) (i) H_0: $\sigma^2 = 50$ H_a: $\sigma^2 \neq 50$ $\alpha = 0.10$

Observed value: $\chi^2 = \dfrac{(19-1)(33.3)}{50} = 11.99$, df = 18.

Critical values: $\chi^2 = 9.39$, $\chi^2 = 28.869$. Decision: fail
  to reject H_0.
  (ii) type II.

  (d) (i) H_0: $\sigma^2 \leq 30$ H_a: $\sigma^2 > 30$ $\alpha = 0.10$

Observed value: $\chi^2 = \dfrac{(9-1)(45)}{30} = 12$, df = 8.

Critical value: $\chi^2 = 13.362$. Decision: fail to reject
  H_0.
  (ii) type II.

9.19 (e) (i) H_0: $\sigma^2 \geq 65$ H_a: $\sigma^2 < 65$ $\alpha = 0.05$

Observed value: $\chi^2 = \dfrac{(22-1)(40.2)}{65} = 12.99$, df = 21.

Critical value: $\chi^2 = 11.591$. Decision: fail to reject H_0.

     (ii) type II.

(f) (i) H_0: $\sigma^2 = 20$ H_a: $\sigma^2 \neq 20$ $\alpha = 0.01$

Observed value: $\chi^2 = \dfrac{(26-1)(38.4)}{20} = 48$, df = 25.

Critical values: $\chi^2 = 10.52$, $\chi^2 = 46.928$. Decision: reject H_0.

     (ii) type I.

9.20 H_0: $\sigma^2 \leq (0.70)^2 = 0.49$ H_a: $\sigma^2 > 0.49$ $\alpha = 0.05$

Observed value: $\chi^2 = \dfrac{(20-1)(0.94)^2}{0.49} = 34.26$, df = 19.

Critical value: $\chi^2 = 30.144$. Decision: reject H_0. The data indicate that the standard deviation is more than 0.7.

9.21 H_0: $\sigma^2 \leq 0.0001$ H_a: $\sigma^2 > 0.0001$ $\alpha = 0.01$

Observed value: $\chi^2 = \dfrac{(15-1)(0.0002)}{0.0001} = 28$, df = 14.

Critical value: $\chi^2 = 29.141$. Decision: fail to reject H_0. There is insufficient evidence to indicate that the variability has increased.

9.22 H_0: $\sigma^2 = 4$ H_a: $\sigma^2 \neq 4$ $\alpha = 0.05$

Observed value: $\chi^2 = \dfrac{(20-1)(6)}{4} = 28.5$, df = 19.

Critical values: $\chi^2 = 8.907$, $\chi^2 = 32.852$.
Decision: fail to reject H_0. The data do not indicate a difference in the variance.

9.23 H_0: $\sigma^2 \leq (3)^2 = 9$ H_a: $\sigma^2 > 9$ $\alpha = 0.01$

Observed value: $\chi^2 = \dfrac{(12-1)(23)}{9} = 28.11$, df = 11.

Critical value: $\chi^2 = 24.725$. Decision: reject H_0. Based on this information, the company will not market the speedometer.

9.24 $s^2 = \dfrac{n(\sum x^2) - (\sum x)^2}{n(n-1)} = \dfrac{9(74308) - (814)^2}{(9)(8)} = 85.78$

$H_0: \sigma^2 \geq 156 \qquad H_a: \sigma^2 < 156 \qquad \alpha = 0.01$

Observed value: $\chi^2 = \dfrac{(9-1)(85.78)}{156} = 4.4, \quad df = 8$

Critical value: $\chi^2 = 1.646$. Decision: fail to reject H_0. The data do not support the claim that the variance is less than 156.

9.25 $\dfrac{(28-1)(1.6)^2}{40.113} < \sigma^2 < \dfrac{(28-1)(1.6)^2}{16.151}$ or $1.72 < \sigma^2 < 4.28$.

9.26 $s^2 = \dfrac{n\sum x^2 - (\sum x)^2}{n(n-1)} = \dfrac{(6)(123764) - (860)^2}{(6)(5)} = 99.47$

$\dfrac{(6-1)(99.47)}{12.833} < \sigma^2 < \dfrac{(6-1)(99.47)}{0.831}$ or $38.76 < \sigma^2 < 598.5$.

9.27 (a) $\dfrac{(20-1)(0.94)^2}{30.144} < \sigma^2 < \dfrac{(20-1)(0.94)^2}{10.117}$ or $0.56 < \sigma^2 < 1.66$

(b) $\dfrac{(15-1)(0.0002)}{29.141} < \sigma^2 < \dfrac{(15-1)(0.0002)}{4.66}$ or $0.0001 < \sigma^2 < 0.0006$

(c) $\dfrac{(12-1)(23)}{26.757} < \sigma^2 < \dfrac{(12-1)(23)}{2.603}$ or $9.46 < \sigma^2 < 97.2$

9.28 (a) 2.764 (b) 1.714 (c) 1.345 (d) 2.08

9.29 $H_0: \mu \leq 150 \qquad H_a: \mu > 150 \qquad \alpha = 0.05$

Observed value: $t = \dfrac{151.2 - 150}{(2.4)/\sqrt{14}} = 1.87, \quad df = 13$.

Critical value: $t = 1.771$. Decision: reject H_0. The data indicate that the mean number of calories per can is more than 150 ounces.

9.30 $H_0: \mu = 11 \qquad H_a: \mu \neq 11 \qquad \alpha = 0.10$

Observed value: $t = \dfrac{11.5 - 11}{\sqrt{2.25}/\sqrt{20}} = 1.49, \quad df = 19$.

Critical values: $t = \pm 1.729$. Decision: fail to reject H_0. The data do not support the manufacturer's claim that the mean percentage of sodium carbonate is different from 11%.

9.31 H_0: $\mu = 0.12$ H_a: $\mu \neq 0.12$ $\alpha = 0.10$

Observed value: $z = \dfrac{0.114 - 0.12}{0.015/\sqrt{18}} = -1.7$

Critical values: $z = \pm 1.65$. Decision: reject H_0. The data suggest that the mean diameter is different.

9.32 H_0: $\mu \geq 600$ H_a: $\mu < 600$ $\alpha = 0.05$

Observed value: $t = \dfrac{450 - 600}{300/\sqrt{15}} = -1.94$,   df = 14.

Critical value: $t = -1.761$. Decision: reject H_0. The data indicate that the mean tax deduction for charities is less than \$600.

9.33 H_0: $\mu \leq 55$ H_a: $\mu > 55$

Observed value: $t = \dfrac{65 - 55}{17/\sqrt{14}} = 2.2$,   df = 13.

$0.01 < $ P-value $= P(t \geq 2.2) < 0.025$.

It follows that the null hypothesis would be rejected for any level α as large or larger than 0.025. We would fail to reject the null hypothesis for any level α as small or smaller than 0.01.

9.34 $\bar{x} = \sum x/n = 2269/15 = 151.27$. $s = \sqrt{\dfrac{n\left(\sum x^2\right) - \left(\sum x\right)^2}{n(n-1)}}$

$= \sqrt{\dfrac{(15)(354059) - (2269)^2}{(15)(14)}} = 27.82$

H_0: $\mu \leq 130$ H_a: $\mu > 130$ $\alpha = 0.05$

Observed value: $t = \dfrac{151.27 - 130}{27.82/\sqrt{15}} = 2.96$,   df = 14.

Critical value: $t = 1.761$. Decision: reject H_0. The data indicate that the mean is more than 130.

9.35 $\bar{x} = \sum x/n = 1096/7 = 156.57.$ $\qquad s = \sqrt{\dfrac{n(\sum x^2) - (\sum x)^2}{n(n-1)}}$

$$= \sqrt{\dfrac{(7)(173072) - (1096)^2}{(7)(6)}} = 15.65.$$

(a) $156.57 \pm (1.943)(15.65/\sqrt{7})$ or $145.08 < \mu < 168.06.$

(b) $(1.943)(15.65/\sqrt{7}) = 11.49.$

9.36 (a) $151.2 \pm (2.160)(2.4/\sqrt{14})$ or $149.81 < \mu < 152.59.$

(b) $11.5 \pm (1.729)(\sqrt{2.25}/\sqrt{20})$ or $10.92 < \mu < 12.08.$

(c) $0.114 \pm (2.58)(0.015/\sqrt{18})$ or $0.105 < \mu < 0.123.$

9.37 (a) 26.217   (b) 30.144   (c) 16.791   (d) 69.126

9.38 $H_0: \sigma^2 \geq 9$ $H_a: \sigma^2 < 9$ $\alpha = 0.01$

Observed value: $\chi^2 = \dfrac{(14-1)(5.76)}{9} = 8.32,$ df = 13.

Critical value: $\chi^2 = 4.107.$ Decision: fail to reject H_0. There is not sufficient evidence to suggest the variance is less than 9.

9.39 $H_0: \sigma^2 \leq 5.10$ $H_a: \sigma^2 > 5.10$ $\alpha = 0.10$

Observed value: $\chi^2 = \dfrac{(10-1)(2.58)^2}{5.10} = 11.75,$ df = 9.

Critical value: $\chi^2 = 14.684.$ Decision: fail to reject H_0. There is insufficient evidence to support the claim that the variance is more than 5.10.

9.40 (a) $\dfrac{(14-1)(5.76)}{29.819} < \sigma^2 < \dfrac{(14-1)(5.76)}{3.565}$ or $2.51 < \sigma^2 < 21.$

(b) $\dfrac{(10-1)(2.58)^2}{16.919} < \sigma^2 < \dfrac{(10-1)(2.58)^2}{3.325}$ or $3.54 < \sigma^2 < 18.02$

9.41 (a) $H_0: \mu \geq 75$ $H_a: \mu < 75$ $\alpha = 0.05$

Observed value: $t = \dfrac{70 - 75}{(6.75)/\sqrt{8}} = -2.10,$ df = 7.

Critical value: $t = -1.895.$ Decision: reject H_0.

(b) $\alpha = 0.01.$ Observed value: $t = -2.10,$ df = 7.

Critical value: $t = -2.998.$ Decision: fail to reject H_0.

9.42 (a) The conclusion reached in part (a).

(b) (i) $H_0: \mu \geq 75$ $H_a: \mu < 75$ $\alpha = 0.05$

Observed value: $t = \dfrac{70 - 75}{10/\sqrt{8}} = -1.41$, df = 7.

Critical value: $t = -1.895$. Decision: fail to reject H_0.

(ii) $\alpha = 0.01$. Observed value: $t = -1.41$, df = 7.
Critical value: $t = -2.998$. Decision: fail to reject H_0.

9.43 (a) The conclusion reached in part (b).

(b) (i) $H_0: \mu \geq 75$ $H_a: \mu < 75$ $\alpha = 0.05$

Observed value: $t = \dfrac{70 - 75}{(4.50)/\sqrt{8}} = -3.14$, df = 7.

Critical value: $t = -1.895$. Decision: reject H_0.

(ii) $\alpha = 0.01$. Observed value: $t = -3.14$, df = 7.

Critical value: $t = -2.998$. Decision: reject H_0.

9.44 (a) The conclusion reached in part (b).

(b) (i) $H_0: \mu \geq 75$ $H_a: \mu < 75$ $\alpha = 0.05$

Observed value: $t = \dfrac{67 - 75}{(6.75)/\sqrt{8}} = -3.35$, df = 7.

Critical value: $t = -1.895$. Decision: reject H_0.

(ii) $\alpha = 0.01$. Observed value: $t = -3.35$, df = 7.
Critical value: $t = -2.998$. Decision: reject H_0.

9.45 (a) The conclusion reached in part (a).

(b) (i) $H_0: \mu \geq 75$ $H_a: \mu < 75$ $\alpha = 0.05$

Observed value: $t = \dfrac{72 - 75}{(6.75)/\sqrt{8}} = -1.26$, df = 7.

Critical value: $t = -1.895$. Decision: fail to reject H_0.

(ii) $\alpha = 0.01$. Observed value: $t = -1.26$, df = 7.
Critical value: $t = -2.998$. Decision: fail to reject H_0.

9.46 (a) $70 \pm (2.365)(6.75/\sqrt{8})$ or $64.36 < \mu < 75.64$.

(b) (i) longer   (ii) shorter   (iii) same   (iv) same

9.47 10   15   20   25

9.48 (a)

b	$P(z^2 < b)$	
0.455	2(0.2486)	= 0.50
1.638	2(0.3997)	= 0.80
2.706	2(0.4495)	= 0.90
3.841	2(0.475)	= 0.95
6.635	2(0.4951)	= 0.99

(b) They are the same.

10.1

	F(0.01)	F(0.025)	F(0.05)
(a)	6.63	4.82	3.69
(b)	10.29	6.76	4.82
(c)	4.41	3.42	2.77
(d)	12.25	8.07	5.59

(e) 4.01   (f) 4.77   (g) 3.13   (h) 3.07

10.2 (a) (i) $H_0: \sigma_A^2 = \sigma_B^2$ $H_a: \sigma_A^2 \neq \sigma_B^2$ $\alpha = 0.05$

Observed value: $F = 43/10 = 4.3$, df = (10,7).
Critical value: F = 4.76.
Decision: fail to reject H_0.

(ii) type II

(b) (i) $H_0: \sigma_A^2 = \sigma_B^2$ $H_a: \sigma_A^2 \neq \sigma_B^2$ $\alpha = 0.05$

Observed value: $F = 43/10 = 4.3$, df = (7,10).
Critical value: F = 3.95.
Decision: reject H_0.

(ii) type I

(c) (i) $H_0: \sigma_A^2 \leq \sigma_B^2$ $H_a: \sigma_A^2 > \sigma_B^2$ $\alpha = 0.01$

Observed value: $F = 20/5 = 4$, df = (30,20).
Critical value: F = 2.78.
Decision: reject H_0.

(ii) type I

(d) (i) $H_0: \sigma_A^2 \leq \sigma_B^2$ $H_a: \sigma_A^2 > \sigma_B^2$ $\alpha = 0.05$

Observed value: $F = 20/8 = 2.5$, df = (30,20).
Critical value: F = 2.04.
Decision: reject H_0.

(ii) type I

(e) (i) $H_0: \sigma_A^2 = \sigma_B^2$ $H_a: \sigma_A^2 \neq \sigma_B^2$ $\alpha = 0.10$

Observed value: $F = 100/10 = 10$, df = (4,9).
Critical value: F = 3.63.
Decision: reject H_0.

(ii) type I

10.2   (f)   (i) $H_0: \sigma_A^2 \leq \sigma_B^2$ $H_a: \sigma_A^2 > \sigma_B^2$ $\alpha = 0.01$

Observed value: $F = 100/10 = 10$,   df $= (9,4)$.
Critical value: $F = 14.66$.
Decision: fail to reject H_0.

(ii)   type II

10.3   (a) $\dfrac{(43/10)}{4.76} < \dfrac{\sigma_A^2}{\sigma_B^2} < (43/10)(3.95)$ or $0.9 < \sigma_A^2/\sigma^2{}_B < 16.99$.

(b) $\dfrac{(43/10)}{3.95} < \dfrac{\sigma_A^2}{\sigma_B^2} < (43/10)(4.76)$ or $1.09 < \sigma_A^2/\sigma_B^2 < 20.47$.

(c) $\dfrac{(20/5)}{2.78} < \dfrac{\sigma_A^2}{\sigma_B^2} < (20/5)(2.55)$ or $1.44 < \sigma_A^2/\sigma_B^2 < 10.2$.

(d) $\dfrac{(20/8)}{2.04} < \dfrac{\sigma_A^2}{\sigma_B^2} < (20/8)(1.93)$ or $1.23 < \sigma_A^2/\sigma_B^2 < 4.83$.

(e) $\dfrac{(100/10)}{3.63} < \dfrac{\sigma_A^2}{\sigma_B^2} < (100/10)(6)$ or $2.75 < \sigma_A^2/\sigma_B^2 < 60$.

(f) $\dfrac{(100/10)}{14.66} < \dfrac{\sigma_A^2}{\sigma_B^2} < (100/10)(6.42)$ or $0.68 < \sigma_A^2/\sigma_B^2 < 64.2$.

10.4 $H_0: \sigma_A^2 = \sigma_B^2$ $H_a: \sigma_A^2 \neq \sigma_B^2$ $\alpha = 0.10$

Observed value: $F = 1.5/0.6 = 2.5$,   df $= (15,20)$.
Critical value: $F = 2.2$.
Decision: reject H_0. There is sufficient evidence to
indicate a difference in variability between populations
A and B.

10.5 $H_0: \sigma_B^2 \leq \sigma_A^2$ $H_a: \sigma_B^2 > \sigma_A^2$ $\alpha = 0.05$

Observed value: $F = 1.1/0.5 = 2.2$, df $= (24,24)$.
Critical value: $F = 1.98$.
Decision: reject H_0. The data suggest that the vari-
ability of brand A is smaller than that of brand B.

10.6　$H_0: \sigma_A^2 \leq \sigma_B^2$　　　$H_a: \sigma_A^2 > \sigma_B^2$　　　$\alpha = 0.01$

Observed value:　$F = 6/3 = 2$,　$df = (8,8)$.
Critical value:　$F = 6.03$.
Decision:　fail to reject H_0.　There is insufficient
evidence to conclude that the variability of clerk A is
larger than that of clerk B.

10.7　$H_0: \sigma_A^2 \leq \sigma_B^2$　　　$H_a: \sigma_A^2 > \sigma_B^2$　　　$\alpha = 0.05$

Observed value: $F = (13.9)^2/(12.1)^2 = 1.32$,　$df = (30,40)$
Critical value:　$F = 1.74$.　Decision:　fail to reject H_0.
There is insufficient evidence to indicate that the variability in males' systolic blood pressure is larger than
females.

10.8　(a)　The table with sample sizes 41.

　　　(b)　$H_0: \sigma_A^2 \leq \sigma_B^2$　　　$H_a: \sigma_A^2 > \sigma_B^2$　　　$\alpha = 0.05$

　　　　　Observed value:　$F = 100/50 = 2$.
　　　　　Critical value:　$F = 1.69$ with $df = (40,40)$.
　　　　　　　　　　　　　$F = 2.98$ with $df = (10,10)$.
　　　　　Decision:　Reject H_0 when the sample sizes are 41.
　　　　　Fail to reject H_0 when the sample sizes are 11.

10.9　(a)　$H_0: \mu_d = 0$　　　$H_a: \mu_d \neq 0$　　　$\alpha = 0.05$

　　　　　Observed value:　$t = \dfrac{2.38 - 0}{4.78/\sqrt{8}} = 1.41$, $df = 7$.

　　　　　Critical values: $t = \pm 2.365$.　Decision: fail to reject
　　　　　　　　　　　　　　　　　　　　　　　　　　　H_0.

　　　(b)　$H_0: \mu_d \leq 0$　　　$H_a: \mu_d > 0$　　　$\alpha = 0.05$

　　　　　Observed value:　$t = \dfrac{3.5 - 0}{3.02/\sqrt{6}} = 2.84$,　$df = 5$.

　　　　　Critical value:　$t = 2.015$.　Decision:　reject H_0.

　　　(c)　$H_0: \mu_d \geq 0$　　　$H_a: \mu_d < 0$　　　$\alpha = 0.05$

　　　　　Observed value:　$t = \dfrac{-1.86 - 0}{3.72/\sqrt{7}} = -1.32$,　$df = 6$

　　　　　Critical value:　$t = -1.943$.　Decision:　fail to
　　　　　　　　　　　　　　　　　　　　　　　　reject H_0.

10.9 (a) $H_0: \mu_d = 10$ $H_a: \mu_d \neq 10$ $\alpha = 0.10$

Observed value: $t = \dfrac{13.33 - 10}{4.82/\sqrt{9}} = 2.07$, df = 8

Critical values: $t = \pm 1.86$. Decision: reject H_0.

10.10 $H_0: \mu_A - \mu_B \leq 0$ $H_a: \mu_A - \mu_B > 0$ $\alpha = 0.10$

Observed value: $t = \dfrac{2 - 0}{3.16/\sqrt{6}} = 1.55$, df = 5.

Critical value: $t = 1.476$. Decision: reject H_0. There is sufficient evidence to suggest that the advertising program is effective.

10.11 $H_0: \mu_A - \mu_B \leq 0$ $H_a: \mu_A - \mu_B > 0$ $\alpha = 0.05$

Observed value: $t = \dfrac{2 - 0}{(2.31)/\sqrt{7}} = 2.29$, df = 6.

Critical value: $t = 1.943$. Decision: reject H_0. There is sufficient evidence to indicate that the special study program is effective in improving scores.

10.12 (a) $H_0: \mu_A - \mu_B \leq 0$ $H_a: \mu_A - \mu_B > 0$

Observed value: $t = \dfrac{0.225 - 0}{(0.276)/\sqrt{8}} = 2.31$, df = 7.

$0.025 <$ P-value $= P(t \geq 2.31) < 0.05$.

(b) (i) reject H_0 (ii) reject H_0 (iii) fail to reject H_0

10.13 $H_0: \mu_A - \mu_B = 0$ $H_a: \mu_A - \mu_B \neq 0$ $\alpha = 0.05$

Observed value: $t = \dfrac{6 - 0}{8.4/\sqrt{12}} = 2.47$, df = 11.

Critical values: $t = \pm 2.201$. Decision: reject H_0. The data indicate a difference in mean systolic blood pressure levels for the two populations.

10.14 (a) $2.38 \pm (2.365)(4.78/\sqrt{8})$ or $-1.62 < \mu_d < 6.38$.

(b) $3.5 \pm (2.015)(3.02/\sqrt{6})$ or $1.02 < \mu_d < 5.98$.

(c) $-1.86 \pm (1.943)(3.72/\sqrt{7})$ or $-4.59 < \mu_d < 0.87$.

(d) $13.33 \pm (1.86)(4.82/\sqrt{9})$ or $10.34 < \mu_d < 16.32$.

10.15 (a) $2 \pm (1.476)(3.16/\sqrt{6})$ or $0.1 < \mu_A - \mu_B < 3.9$.

(b) $2 \pm (1.943)(2.31/\sqrt{7})$ or $0.3 < \mu_A - \mu_B < 3.7$.

(c) $6 \pm (2.201)(8.4/\sqrt{12})$ or $0.66 < \mu_A - \mu_B < 11.34$.

10.16 (a) The first data set. Note that the d's in the second data set vary much more than the d's in the first data set.

(b) $H_0: \mu_A - \mu_B \leq 0$ $H_a: \mu_A - \mu_B > 0$ $\alpha = 0.05$

Observed value: (First data set) $t = \dfrac{4}{(0.89)/\sqrt{6}} = 11.01$

(Second data set) $t = \dfrac{4}{(7.4)/\sqrt{6}} = 1.32$,

$df = 5$.

Critical value: $t = 2.015$.
Decision: (First data set) reject H_0

(Second data set) fail to reject H_0

10.17 (a) $H_0: \mu_A - \mu_B = 0$ $H_a: \mu_A - \mu_B \neq 0$ $\alpha = 0.05$

Observed value: $z = \dfrac{(175-165) - 0}{\sqrt{\dfrac{360}{40} + \dfrac{350}{50}}} = 2.5$

Critical values: $z = \pm 1.96$. Decision: reject H_0.

(b) (i) no   (ii) yes   (iii) yes

(c) $H_0: \mu_A - \mu_B = 0$ $H_a: \mu_A - \mu_B \neq 0$ $\alpha = 0.01$

Observed value: $z = 2.5$. Critical values: $z = \pm 2.58$
Decision: fail to reject H_0

149

10.18 (a) $H_0: \mu_A - \mu_B \leq 0$ $H_a: \mu_A - \mu_B > 0$ $\alpha = 0.05$

Observed value: $z = \dfrac{(400 - 396) - 0}{\sqrt{\dfrac{210}{35} + \dfrac{105}{35}}} = 1.33$

Critical value: $z = 1.65$.
Decision: fail to reject H_0.

(b) (i) no   (ii) yes   (iii) yes

(c) $H_0: \mu_A - \mu_B \leq 0$ $H_a: \mu_A - \mu_B > 0$ $\alpha = 0.10$

Observed value: $z = 1.33$. Critical value: $z = 1.28$
Decision: reject H_0.

10.19 $H_0: \mu_A - \mu_B \geq 0$ $H_a: \mu_A - \mu_B < 0$ $\alpha = 0.05$

Observed value: $z = \dfrac{(2.80 - 2.98) - 0}{\sqrt{\dfrac{(0.4)^2}{60} + \dfrac{(0.5)^2}{52}}} = -2.08$

Critical value: $z = -1.65$.
Decision: reject H_0. The data indicate that the current year graduates have a higher mean grade point average.

10.20 (a) $H_0: \mu_B - \mu_A = 10$ $H_a: \mu_B - \mu_A \neq 10$ $\alpha = 0.05$

Observed value: $t = \dfrac{(135 - 120) - 10}{\sqrt{\dfrac{(5)(100) + 9(81)}{14}}\sqrt{\dfrac{1}{6} + \dfrac{1}{10}}} = 1.03$,

$df = 14$.

Critical values: $t = \pm 2.145$.
Decision: fail to reject H_0.

(b) $H_0: \mu_A - \mu_B \geq 0$ $H_a: \mu_A - \mu_B < 0$ $\alpha = 0.10$

Observed value: $t = \dfrac{(180-200) - 0}{\sqrt{\dfrac{70}{10} + \dfrac{340}{7}}} = -2.68$, $df = 6$

Critical value: $t = -1.44$. Decision: reject H_0.

10.21   (a) H_0: $\sigma_A^2 = \sigma_B^2$ H_a: $\sigma_A^2 \neq \sigma_B^2$ $\alpha = 0.10$

Observed value: F = 240/205 = 1.17, df = (6,8).
Critical value: F = 3.58. Decision: fail to reject H_0.

(b)   Assume $\sigma_A^2 = \sigma_B^2$. H_0: $\mu_A - \mu_B \leq 0$ H_a: $\mu_A - \mu_B > 0$

$\alpha = 0.10$

Observed value: $t = \dfrac{(166 - 150) - 0}{\sqrt{\dfrac{6(240) + 8(205)}{7 + 9 - 2}}\sqrt{\dfrac{1}{7} + \dfrac{1}{9}}} = 2.14$,

df = 14.

Critical value: t = 1.345. Decision: reject H_0.
The data suggest that the mean completion time
for test A is more than that required for test B.

10.22   (a) H_0: $\sigma_A^2 = \sigma_B^2$ H_a: $\sigma_A^2 \neq \sigma_B^2$ $\alpha = 0.05$

Observed value: F = 0.39/0.10 = 3.9, df = (10,10)
Critical value: F = 3.72. Decision: reject H_0.

(b)   Assume $\sigma_A^2 \neq \sigma_B^2$.

H_0: $\mu_A - \mu_B = 0$ H_a: $\mu_A - \mu_B \neq 0$ $\alpha = 0.05$

Observed value: $t = \dfrac{(3.8 - 3.5) - 0}{\sqrt{\dfrac{0.39}{11} + \dfrac{0.10}{11}}} = 1.42$,   df = 10.

Critical values: t = ±2.228. Decision: fail to
reject H_0. The data do not refute the mayor's claim.

10.23   (a) $(2.8-2.98) \pm (1.65)\sqrt{\dfrac{(.5)^2}{52} + \dfrac{(.4)^2}{60}}$ or $-0.32 < \mu_A - \mu_B < -0.04$

(b) $(180-200) \pm (2.447)\sqrt{\dfrac{70}{10} + \dfrac{340}{7}}$ or $-38.24 < \mu_A - \mu_B < -1.76$.

(c) $(166-150) \pm (1.761)\sqrt{\dfrac{6(240)+8(205)}{7 + 9 - 2}}\sqrt{\dfrac{1}{7} + \dfrac{1}{9}}$

or $2.84 < \mu_A - \mu_B < 29.16$.

Note: In part (b), assume $\sigma_A^2 \neq \sigma_B^2$. Thus, df = 6.

In part (c), assume $\sigma_A^2 = \sigma_B^2$. Thus, df = 14.

151

10.24 $\bar{x}_A = 105/5 = 21$ $\qquad$ $\bar{x}_B = 181.3/7 = 25.9$

$$s_A^2 = \frac{5(2290.86) - (105)^2}{(5)(4)} = 21.465$$

$$s_B^2 = \frac{7(4756.29) - (181.3)^2}{(7)(6)} = 10.103$$

$H_0: \mu_A - \mu_B = 0$ $\qquad$ $H_a: \mu_A - \mu_B \neq 0$ $\qquad$ $\alpha = 0.05$

Observed value: $\quad t = \dfrac{(21 - 25.9) - 0}{\sqrt{\dfrac{4(21.465) + 6(10.103)}{5 + 7 - 2}}\sqrt{\dfrac{1}{5} + \dfrac{1}{7}}} = -2.19$

df = 10

Critical values: $t = \pm 2.228$. Decision: fail to reject H_0.

10.25 $\bar{x}_A = 124.6/5 = 24.92$ $\qquad$ $\bar{x}_B = 120.8/4 = 30.2$

$$s_A^2 = \frac{5(3137.7) - (124.6)^2}{(5)(4)} = 8.167$$

$$s_B^2 = \frac{4(3683.88) - (120.8)^2}{(4)(3)} = 11.907$$

$H_0: \mu_A - \mu_B \geq 0$ $\qquad$ $H_a: \mu_A - \mu_B < 0$ $\qquad$ $\alpha = 0.05$

Observed value: $\quad t = \dfrac{(24.92 - 30.2) - 0}{\sqrt{\dfrac{4(8.167) + 3(11.907)}{5 + 4 - 2}}\sqrt{\dfrac{1}{5} + \dfrac{1}{4}}} = -2.52$

df = 7

Critical value: $t = -1.895$. Decision: reject H_0. The data indicate that the mean percentage of income needed to maintain two homes is less for residents of town A than for town B.

10.26 (a) $H_0: \mu_A - \mu_B \leq 0$ $\qquad$ $H_a: \mu_A - \mu_B > 0$ $\qquad$ $\alpha = 0.01$

Observed value: $\quad z = \dfrac{(125 - 117) - 0}{\sqrt{\dfrac{(13.9)^2}{31} + \dfrac{(12.1)^2}{41}}} = 2.56$

Critical value: $z = 2.33$. Decision: reject H_0. The data indicate that the mean systolic blood pressure of males is larger than females for the 20-24 age group.

10.26 (b) $H_0: \mu_A - \mu_B \leq 0$ $\quad$ $H_a: \mu_A - \mu_B > 0$ $\quad$ $\alpha = 0.01$

Observed value: $\quad z = \dfrac{(75 - 70) - 0}{\sqrt{\dfrac{(10.1)^2}{45} + \dfrac{(9.8)^2}{45}}} = 2.38$

Critical value: $z = 2.33$. Decision: reject H_0. The data indicate that the mean diastolic blood pressure of males is larger than females for the 20-24 age group.

10.27 $H_0: \mu_A - \mu_B = 0$ $\quad$ $H_a: \mu_A - \mu_B \neq 0$ $\quad$ $\alpha = 0.05$

Observed value: $\quad z = \dfrac{(2.10 - 2.45) - 0}{\sqrt{\dfrac{0.64}{45} + \dfrac{0.70}{50}}} = -2.08$

Critical values: $z = \pm 1.96$. Decision: reject H_0. The data indicate that there is a difference in mean grade-point averages of graduating males and females.

10.28 $H_0: \mu_A - \mu_B = 0$ $\quad$ $H_a: \mu_A - \mu_B \neq 0$ $\quad$ $\alpha = 0.01$

Observed value: $\quad z = \dfrac{(820 - 850) - 0}{\sqrt{\dfrac{4900}{35} + \dfrac{6900}{40}}} = -1.7$

Critical values: $z = \pm 2.58$. Decision: fail to reject H_0. There is insufficient evidence to indicate a difference in the mean number of passengers, per trip.

10.29 (a) $H_0: \sigma_A^2 = \sigma_B^2$ $\quad$ $H_a: \sigma_A^2 \neq \sigma_B^2$ $\quad$ $\alpha = 0.05$

Observed value: $F = 80000/40000 = 2$, $\quad$ df $= (12, 12)$

Critical value: $F = 3.28$. Decision: fail to reject H_0. Assume $\sigma_A^2 = \sigma_B^2$.

$\quad\quad H_0: \mu_A - \mu_B \geq 0$ $\quad$ $H_a: \mu_A - \mu_B < 0$ $\quad$ $\alpha = 0.05$

Observed value: $\quad t = \dfrac{25200 - 25375}{\sqrt{\dfrac{(12)(80000) + 12(40000)}{13 + 13 - 2}}\sqrt{\dfrac{1}{13} + \dfrac{1}{13}}} = -1.82$

df $= 24$

Critical value: $t = -1.711$. Decision: reject H_0. There is sufficient evidence to indicate that brand B lasts longer, on average.

10.29 (b) $H_0: \sigma_A^2 = \sigma_B^2$ $\qquad H_a: \sigma_A^2 \neq \sigma_B^2$ $\qquad\qquad \alpha = 0.05$

Observed value: $F = 80000/80000 = 1$, df $= (12,12)$

Critical value: $F = 3.28$. Decision: fail to reject H_0.

Assume $\sigma_A^2 = \sigma_B^2$.

$H_0: \mu_A - \mu_B \geq 0$ $\qquad H_a: \mu_A - \mu_B < 0$ $\qquad \alpha = 0.05$

Observed value: $t = \dfrac{(25200 - 25375) - 0}{\sqrt{\dfrac{(12)(80000)+(12)(80000)}{13 + 13 - 2}}\sqrt{\dfrac{1}{13}+\dfrac{1}{13}}} = -1.58$

$\quad$ df $= 24$

Critical value: $t = -1.711$. Decision: fail to reject H_0. There is insufficient evidence to indicate that brand B lasts longer, on average.

10.30 $H_0: \sigma_A^2 = \sigma_B^2$ $\qquad H_a: \sigma_A^2 \neq \sigma_B^2$ $\qquad \alpha = 0.02$

Observed value: $F = (6.1)^2/(4.7)^2 = 1.68$, df $= (9,9)$.

Critical value: $F = 5.35$. Decision: fail to reject H_0.

Assume $\sigma_A^2 = \sigma_B^2$.

$H_0: \mu_A - \mu_B = 8$ $\qquad H_a: \mu_A - \mu_B \neq 8$ $\qquad \alpha = 0.02$

Observed value: $t = \dfrac{(179.3 - 166.2) - 8}{\sqrt{\dfrac{9(6.1)^2+9(4.7)^2}{10 + 10 - 2}}\sqrt{\dfrac{1}{10}+\dfrac{1}{10}}} = 2.09$, df $= 18$

Critical value: df $= \pm 2.552$. Decision: fail to reject H_0. There is insufficient evidence to indicate that the mean difference in height is not 8 centimeters.

10.31 (1) $H_0: \mu_A - \mu_B = 0$ $\qquad H_a: \mu_A - \mu_B \neq 0$ $\qquad \alpha = 0.05$

Observed value: $z = \dfrac{(23.9 - 25.4) - 0}{\sqrt{\dfrac{(4.6)^2}{34} + \dfrac{(3.6)^2}{34}}} = -1.5$

Critical values: $z = \pm 1.96$. Decision: fail to reject H_0. There is not sufficient evidence to indicate a difference in population means.

10.32 $\bar{x}_A = 79/6 = 13.17.$ $\bar{x}_B = 67/6 = 11.17.$

$$s_A^2 = \frac{6(1213) - (79)^2}{(6)(5)} = 34.57 \qquad s_B^2 = \frac{6(813) - (67)^2}{(6)(5)} = 12.97$$

(a) $H_0: \sigma_A^2 = \sigma_B^2$ $\quad H_a: \sigma_A^2 \neq \sigma_B^2$ $\quad \alpha = 0.10$

Observed value: $F = 34.57/12.97 = 2.67,$ df $= (5,5).$

Critical value: $F = 5.05.$ Decision: fail to reject $H_0.$

(b) Assume $\sigma_A^2 = \sigma_B^2$

$H_0: \mu_A - \mu_B \leq 0$ $\qquad H_a: \mu_A - \mu_B > 0$ $\qquad \alpha = 0.10$

Observed value: $t = \dfrac{(13.17 - 11.17) - 0}{\sqrt{\dfrac{5(34.57) + 5(12.97)}{6 + 6 - 2}}\sqrt{\dfrac{1}{6} + \dfrac{1}{6}}} = 0.71,$ df $= 10.$

Critical value: $t = 1.372.$ Decision: fail to reject $H_0.$
Increased variability offsets the gain in degrees of freedom.

10.33 (a) $(125 - 117) \pm (2.33)\sqrt{\dfrac{(13.9)^2}{31} + \dfrac{(12.1)^2}{41}}$

or $0.7 < \mu_A - \mu_B < 15.3.$

(b) $(2.10 - 2.45) \pm (1.96)\sqrt{\dfrac{.64}{45} + \dfrac{.70}{50}}$ or $-0.68 < \mu_A - \mu_B < -0.02.$

(c) $(179.3 - 166.2) \pm (2.552)\sqrt{\dfrac{9(6.1)^2 + 9(4.7)^2}{10 + 10 - 2}}\sqrt{\dfrac{1}{10} + \dfrac{1}{10}}$

or $6.89 < \mu_A - \mu_B < 19.31.$

(d) The 95% confidence interval does not contain 0. Therefore, $H_0: \mu_A - \mu_B = 0$ is rejected at the 5% significance level.

10.34 (a) $\hat{p}_1 = 175/250 = 0.7.$ $\quad \hat{p}_2 = 135/175 = 0.771.$

$\hat{p} = (175 + 135)/(250 + 175) = 0.729.$

$H_0: p_1 - p_2 = 0$ $\qquad H_a: p_1 - p_2 \neq 0$ $\qquad \alpha = 0.05$

Observed value: $z = \dfrac{0.7 - 0.771}{\sqrt{(0.729)(0.271)(\frac{1}{250} + \frac{1}{175})}} = -1.63$

Critical values: $z = \pm 1.96.$ Decision: fail to reject $H_0.$

10.34 (b) $\hat{p}_1 = 195/375 = 0.52$ $\hat{p}_2 = 150/325 = 0.462$

$\hat{p} = (195 + 150)/(375 + 325) = 0.493$

$H_0: p_1 - p_2 \leq 0$ $H_a: p_1 - p_2 > 0$ $\alpha = 0.10$

Observed value: $z = \dfrac{0.52 - 0.462}{\sqrt{(0.493)(0.507)(\frac{1}{375} + \frac{1}{325})}} = 1.54$

Critical value: $z = 1.28$. Decision: reject H_0.

(c) $\hat{p}_1 = 205/400 = 0.513$ $\hat{p}_2 = 175/425 = 0.412$

$H_0: p_1 - p_2 = 0.05$ $H_a: p_1 - p_2 \neq 0.05$ $\alpha = 0.05$

Observed value: $z = \dfrac{(0.513 - 0.412) - 0.05}{\sqrt{\frac{(0.513)(0.487)}{400} + \frac{(0.412)(0.588)}{425}}} = 1.48$

Critical value: $z = \pm 1.96$. Decision: fail to reject H_0.

10.35 (a) $(0.7 - 0.771) \pm (1.96)\sqrt{\dfrac{(0.7)(0.3)}{250} + \dfrac{(0.771)(0.229)}{175}}$

or $-0.155 < p_1 - p_2 < 0.013$

(b) $(0.52 - 0.462) \pm (1.28)\sqrt{\dfrac{(0.52)(0.48)}{375} + \dfrac{(0.462)(0.538)}{325}}$

or $0.01 < p_1 - p_2 < 0.107$

(c) $(0.513 - 0.412) \pm (1.65)\sqrt{\dfrac{(0.513)(0.487)}{400} + \dfrac{(0.412)(0.588)}{425}}$

or $0.044 < p_1 - p_2 < 0.158$

10.36 (a) $(50 + 95)/(150 + 200) = 0.414$

(b) $\hat{p}_A = 50/150 = 0.333$ $\hat{p}_B = 95/200 = 0.475$

$H_0: p_A - p_B = 0$ $H_a: p_A - p_B \neq 0$ $\alpha = 0.01$

Observed value: $z = \dfrac{(0.333 - 0.475) - 0}{\sqrt{(0.414)(0.586)(\frac{1}{150} + \frac{1}{200})}} = -2.66$

10.36 (b) Continued:

Critical values: $z = +2.58$. Decision: reject H_0. There appears to be a difference in the population proportions between faculty members at the two universities earning more than $20,000.

10.37 Let A and B refer to eastern and western respectively.

(a) $(90 + 80)/(150 + 150) = 0.567$.

(b) $H_0: p_A - p_B = 0$ $H_a: p_A - p_B \neq 0$ $\alpha = 0.05$

Observed value: $z = \dfrac{0.6 - 0.533}{\sqrt{(0.567)(0.433)(\frac{1}{150} + \frac{1}{150})}} = 1.17$

Critical values: $z = +1.96$. Decision: fail to reject H_0. There is insufficient evidence to indicate a difference in her support between the two regions.

10.38 $\hat{p}_1 = 70/125 = 0.56$ $\hat{p}_2 = 130/200 = 0.65$

$\hat{p} = (70 + 130)/(125 + 200) = 0.615$

$H_0: p_1 - p_2 = 0$ $H_a: p_1 - p_2 \neq 0$ $\alpha = 0.01$

$z = \dfrac{(0.56 - 0.65) - 0}{\sqrt{(0.615)(0.385)(\frac{1}{125} + \frac{1}{200})}} = -1.62$

Critical values: $z = +2.58$. Decision: fail to reject H_0. There is insufficient evidence to indicate a difference in population proportions of workers satisfied in factories A and B.

10.39 Let A and B represent pre and post modifications respectively.

$\hat{p}_A = 20/100 = 0.2$ $\hat{p}_B = 10/100 = 0.1$

$\hat{p} = (20 + 10)/(100 + 100) = 0.15$

$H_0: p_A - p_B \leq 0$ $H_a: p_A - p_B > 0$ $\alpha = 0.05$

Observed value: $z = \dfrac{(0.2 - 0.1) - 0}{\sqrt{(0.15)(0.85)(\frac{1}{100} + \frac{1}{100})}} = 1.98$

Critical value: $z = 1.65$. Decision: reject H_0. The data support the manufacturer's claim that the modification improved quality.

10.40 (a) $(0.333 - 0.475) \pm (2.58)\sqrt{\dfrac{(0.333)(0.667)}{150} + \dfrac{(0.475)(0.525)}{200}}$

or $-0.277 < p_1 - p_2 < -0.007$

(b)
$(0.6 - 0.533) \pm (1.96)\sqrt{\dfrac{(0.6)(0.4)}{150} + \dfrac{(0.533)(0.467)}{150}}$

or $-0.045 < p_1 - p_2 < 0.179$.

10.41 (a) Data set 1: $\hat{p}_1 = 5/100 = 0.05$, $\hat{p}_2 = 9/120 = 0.075$
Data set 2: $\hat{p}_1 = 30/600 = 0.05$, $\hat{p}_2 = 54/720 = 0.075$

(b) $\hat{p} = (30 + 54)/(600 + 720) = 0.064$.

$H_0: p_1 - p_2 \geq 0 \qquad H_a: p_1 - p_2 < 0 \qquad \alpha = 0.05$

Observed value: $z = \dfrac{(0.05 - 0.075) - 0}{\sqrt{(0.064)(0.936)(\frac{1}{600} + \frac{1}{720})}} = -1.85$

Critical value: $z = -1.65$. Decision: reject H_0. A larger sample size makes it more likely to reject a false null hypothesis.

10.42

	F(.01)	F(.025)	F(.05)
(a)	6.42	4.72	3.63
(b)	14.66	8.90	6.00
(c)	2.20	1.94	1.74

10.43 $H_0: \sigma_A^2 = \sigma_B^2 \qquad H_a: \sigma_A^2 \neq \sigma_B^2 \qquad \alpha = 0.05$

Observed value: $F = (4.6)^2/(4.5)^2 = 1.04$, df $= (33,27)$

Critical value: $F = 2.13$. Decision: fail to reject H_0. There is insufficient evidence to indicate a difference in population variances.

10.44 $H_0: \sigma_A^2 = \sigma_B^2 \qquad H_a: \sigma_A^2 \neq \sigma_B^2 \qquad \alpha = 0.02$

Observed value: $F = (5.6)^2/(3.7)^2 = 2.29$, df $= (9,9)$

Critical value: $F = 5.35$. Decision: fail to reject H_0. The data do not refute the instructor's claim.

10.45 $H_0: \sigma_A^2 \leq \sigma_B^2$ $\qquad$ $H_a: \sigma_A^2 > \sigma_B^2$ $\qquad\qquad$ $\alpha = 0.05$

Observed value: $F = (10.1)^2/(9.8)^2 = 1.06$, df $= (44,44)$

Critical value: $F = 1.69$. Decision: fail to reject H_0. The data do not support the nurse's claim that the variability in males' diastolic blood pressure is larger than that of females.

10.46 (a) $\dfrac{(4.5)^2}{(4.6)^2}\left(\dfrac{1}{2.47}\right) < \dfrac{\sigma_B^2}{\sigma_A^2} < \dfrac{(4.5)^2}{(4.6)^2}(2.47)$

$\qquad$ or $0.387 < \sigma_B^2/\sigma_A^2 < 2.364$

Therefore $1/12.255 < \sigma_A^2/\sigma_B^2 < 1/0.428$

or $0.082 < \sigma_A^2/\sigma_B^2 < 2.336$.

$\qquad$ (b) $\dfrac{(5.6)^2}{(3.7)^2}\left(\dfrac{1}{3.18}\right) < \dfrac{\sigma_A^2}{\sigma_B^2} < \dfrac{(5.6)^2}{(3.7)^2}(3.18)$

$\qquad$ or $0.72 < \sigma_A^2/\sigma_B^2 < 7.284$.

10.47 $H_0: \mu_A - \mu_B \geq 0$ $\qquad$ $H_a: \mu_A - \mu_B < 0$ $\qquad$ $\alpha = 0.05$

Observed value: $t = \dfrac{-1.390 - 0}{1.896/\sqrt{10}} = -2.318$, $\quad$ df $= 9$.

Critical value: $t = -1.833$. Decision: reject H_0. The data suggest that it is quicker to go by car, on average.

10.48 $H_0: \mu_A - \mu_B = 0$ $\qquad$ $H_a: \mu_A - \mu_B \neq 0$ $\qquad$ $\alpha = 0.05$

Observed value: $t = \dfrac{1.57}{3.51/\sqrt{7}} = 1.18$, $\quad$ df $= 6$.

Critical values: $t = +2.447$. Decision: fail to reject H_0. The data do not indicate a difference in the effectiveness of fertilizers.

10.49 (a) $-1.39 \pm (1.833)(1.896/\sqrt{10})$ or $-2.489 < \mu_A - \mu_B < -0.291$.

$\qquad$ (b) $1.57 \pm (2.447)(3.51/\sqrt{7})$ or $-1.676 < \mu_A - \mu_B < 4.816$.

10.50 (a) $H_0: \mu_A - \mu_B = 0$ $H_a: \mu_A - \mu_B \neq 0$ $\alpha = 0.05$

Observed value: $z = \dfrac{(315 - 324) - 0}{\sqrt{\dfrac{400}{40} + \dfrac{360}{60}}} = -2.25$

Critical values: $z = \pm 1.96$. Decision: reject H_0.

(b) $H_0: \mu_A - \mu_B \geq 0$ $H_a: \mu_A - \mu_B < 0$ $\alpha = 0.01$

Observed value: $z = \dfrac{(400 - 410) - 0}{\sqrt{\dfrac{540}{60} + \dfrac{800}{50}}} = -2$

Critical value: $z = -2.33$. Decision: fail to reject H_0.

10.51 $H_0: \mu_A - \mu_B = 0$ $H_a: \mu_A - \mu_B \neq 0$ $\alpha = 0.01$

Observed value: $z = \dfrac{(37.4 - 41.8) - 0}{\sqrt{\dfrac{(4.9)^2}{30} + \dfrac{(5.7)^2}{33}}} = -3.29$

Critical values: $z = \pm 2.58$. Decision: reject H_0. There is sufficient evidence to indicate a difference in population means.

10.52 $H_0: \mu_A - \mu_B \geq 0$ $H_a: \mu_A - \mu_B < 0$ $\alpha = 0.01$

Observed value: $z = \dfrac{(7.1 - 7.95) - 0}{\sqrt{\dfrac{(1.90)^2}{40} + \dfrac{(1.65)^2}{40}}} = -2.14$

Critical value: $z = -2.33$. Decision: fail to reject H_0. There is insufficient evidence to indicate that factory B pays better, on average. P-value = $P(z \leq 2.14) = 0.0162$.

10.53 (a) $H_0: \sigma_A^2 = \sigma_B^2$ $H_a: \sigma_A^2 \neq \sigma_B^2$ $\alpha = 0.05$

Observed value: $F = 60/40 = 1.5$, df = $(9,12)$

Critical value: $F = 3.44$. Decision: fail to reject H_0.

Assume $\sigma_A^2 = \sigma_B^2$.

$H_0: \mu_A - \mu_B \geq 0$ $H_a: \mu_A - \mu_B < 0$ $\alpha = 0.05$

10.53 (a) Continued:

Observed value: $t = \dfrac{(74 - 81) - 0}{\sqrt{\dfrac{(9)(60) + (12)(40)}{10 + 13 - 2}}\sqrt{\dfrac{1}{10} + \dfrac{1}{13}}} = -2.39$

$df = 21.$

Critical value: $t = -1.721$. Decision: reject H_0.

(b) $H_0: \sigma_A^2 = \sigma_B^2$ $H_a: \sigma_A^2 \neq \sigma_B^2$ $\alpha = 0.10$

Observed value: $F = 300/60 = 5$, $df = (20,9)$.

Critical value: $F = 2.94$. Decision: reject H_0.

Assume $\sigma_A^2 \neq \sigma_B^2$.

$H_0: \mu_A - \mu_B \leq 0$ $H_a: \mu_A - \mu_B > 0$ $\alpha = 0.10$

Observed value: $t = \dfrac{(150 - 140) - 0}{\sqrt{\dfrac{60}{10} + \dfrac{300}{21}}} = 2.22$, $df = 9$.

Critical value: $t = 1.383$. Decision: reject H_0.

10.54 $H_0: \sigma_A^2 = \sigma_B^2$ $H_a: \sigma_A^2 \neq \sigma_B^2$ $\alpha = 0.02$

Observed value: $F = \dfrac{(6.8)^2}{(4.4)^2} = 2.39$, $df = (9,9)$.

Critical value: $F = 5.35$. Decision: fail to reject H_0.

Assume $\sigma_A^2 = \sigma_B^2$.

$H_0: \mu_B - \mu_A = 5$ $H_a: \mu_B - \mu_A \neq 5$ $\alpha = 0.02$

Observed value: $t = \dfrac{(48.1 - 39.6) - 5}{\sqrt{\dfrac{9(6.8)^2 + 9(4.4)^2}{10 + 10 - 2}}\sqrt{\dfrac{1}{10} + \dfrac{1}{10}}} = 1.37,$ $df = 18.$

Critical value: $t = \pm 2.552$. Decision: fail to reject H_0.
The data do not refute the claim of the track coach.

10.55 $H_0: \sigma_A^2 = \sigma_B^2$ $H_a: \sigma_A^2 \neq \sigma_B^2$ $\alpha = 0.05$

Observed value: $F = 1.4/1.25 = 1.12$, $df = (9,9)$.

Critical value: $F = 4.03$. Decision: fail to reject H_0.

10.55 Continued:

Assume $\sigma_A^2 = \sigma_B^2$.

$H_0: \mu_A - \mu_B \geq 0$ $\qquad$ $H_a: \mu_A - \mu_B < 0$ $\qquad$ $\alpha = 0.05$

Observed value: $t = \dfrac{(5.1 - 5.9) - 0}{\sqrt{\dfrac{9(1.25) + 9(1.40)}{10 + 10 - 2}}\sqrt{\dfrac{1}{10} + \dfrac{1}{10}}} = -1.55,$ $\qquad$ df = 18.

Critical value: $t = -1.734$. Decision: fail to reject H_0. The data do not indicate that the drug reduces the mean time for rats to complete the maze.

10.56 $\bar{x}_A = 541/7 = 77.29$ $\qquad\qquad$ $\bar{x}_B = 527/7 = 75.29$

$s_A^2 = \dfrac{7(42431) - (541)^2}{(7)(6)} = 103.24$ $\qquad$ $s_B^2 = \dfrac{7(40283) - (527)^2}{(7)(6)} = 101.24$

$H_0: \sigma_A^2 = \sigma_B^2$ $\qquad$ $H_a: \sigma_A^2 \neq \sigma_B^2$ $\qquad$ $\alpha = 0.05$

Observed value: $F = 103.24/101.24 = 1.02$, $\quad$ df = (6,6).

Critical value: $F = 5.82$. Decision: fail to reject H_0.

Assume $\sigma_A^2 = \sigma_B^2$

$H_0: \mu_A - \mu_B \leq 0$ $\qquad$ $H_a: \mu_A - \mu_B > 0$ $\qquad$ $\alpha = 0.05$

Observed value: $t = \dfrac{(77.29 - 75.29) - 0}{\sqrt{\dfrac{6(103.24) + 6(101.24)}{7 + 7 - 2}}\sqrt{\dfrac{1}{7} + \dfrac{1}{7}}} = 0.37,$ $\qquad$ df = 12.

Critical value: $t = 1.782$. Decision: fail to reject H_0.

10.57 (a) $(315 - 324) \pm (1.96)\sqrt{\dfrac{400}{40} + \dfrac{360}{60}}$

or $-16.84 < \mu_A - \mu_B < -1.16$.

(b) $(74 - 81) \pm (2.518)\sqrt{\dfrac{9(60) + 12(40)}{10 + 13 - 2}}\sqrt{\dfrac{1}{10} + \dfrac{1}{13}}$

or $-14.38 < \mu_A - \mu_B < 0.38$.

(c) $(150 - 140) \pm (1.833)\sqrt{\dfrac{60}{10} + \dfrac{300}{21}}$ or $1.74 < \mu_A - \mu_B < 18.26$.

10.58 Let A and B represent students and faculty respectively.

$\hat{p}_A = 70/200 = 0.35$ $\hat{p}_B = 45/100 = 0.45$

$$\hat{p} = (70 + 45)/(200 + 100) = 0.383.$$

$H_0: p_A - p_B = 0$ $H_a: p_A - p_B \neq 0$ $\alpha = 0.05$

Observed value: $z = \dfrac{(0.35 - 0.45) - 0}{\sqrt{(0.383)(0.617)(\frac{1}{200} + \frac{1}{100})}} = -1.68$

Critical values: $z = +1.96$. Decision: fail to reject H_0. There is insufficient evidence to indicate a difference of opinion between students and faculty.

10.59 Let A and B represent men and women respectively.

$\hat{p}_A = 130/250 = 0.52$ $\hat{p}_B = 104/260 = 0.4$

$$\hat{p} = (130 + 104)/(250 + 260) = 0.459$$

$H_0: p_A - p_B = 0$ $H_a: p_A - p_B \neq 0$ $\alpha = 0.01$

Observed value: $z = \dfrac{(0.52 - 0.4) - 0}{\sqrt{(0.459)(0.541)(\frac{1}{250} + \frac{1}{260})}} = 2.72$

Critical values: $z = +2.58$. Decision: reject H_0. The data suggest a difference in attitudes between men and women.

10.60 $\hat{p}_A = 0.06 = \dfrac{x_A}{300}$ so $x_A = 18$ $\hat{p}_B = 0.04 = \dfrac{x_B}{300}$ so $x_B = 12$

$\hat{p} = (18 + 12)/(300 + 300) = 0.05$

$H_0: p_A - p_B = 0$ $H_a: p_A - p_B \neq 0$ $\alpha = 0.05$

Observed value: $z = \dfrac{(0.06 - 0.04) - 0}{\sqrt{(0.05)(0.95)(\frac{1}{300} + \frac{1}{300})}} = 1.12$

Critical values: $z = \pm 1.96$. Decision: fail to reject H_0. There is not enough evidence to suggest a difference in the population proportions of defectives produced by the two shifts.

163

10.61 (a) $(0.35 - 0.45) \pm (1.96) \sqrt{\dfrac{(0.35)(0.65)}{200} + \dfrac{(0.45)(0.55)}{100}}$

or $-0.218 < p_A - p_B < 0.018$

(b) $(0.52 - 0.4) \pm (2.58) \sqrt{\dfrac{(0.52)(0.48)}{250} + \dfrac{(0.4)(0.6)}{260}}$

or $0.007 < p_A - p_B < 0.233$

(c) $(0.06 - 0.04) \pm (1.96) \sqrt{\dfrac{(0.06)(0.94)}{300} + \dfrac{(0.04)(0.96)}{300}}$

or $-0.015 < p_A - p_B < 0.055.$

10.62 In each case, $\hat{p}_A = 0.4$ $\qquad \hat{p}_B = 0.5$ $\qquad \hat{p} = 0.45$

(a) (i) $z = \dfrac{(0.4 - 0.5) - 0}{\sqrt{(0.45)(0.55)(\frac{1}{100} + \frac{1}{100})}} = -1.42$

(ii) $z = \dfrac{(0.4 - 0.5) - 0}{\sqrt{(0.45)(0.55)(\frac{1}{200} + \frac{1}{200})}} = -2.01$

(iii) $z = \dfrac{(0.4 - 0.5) - 0}{\sqrt{(0.45)(0.55)(\frac{1}{500} + \frac{1}{500})}} = -3.18$

(b) Same in each case.

10.63

df for F	df for t	F(.05)	t(.025)	t²(.025)
(1,3)	3	10.13	3.182	10.13
(1,6)	6	5.99	2.447	5.99
(1,8)	8	5.32	2.306	5.32
(1,10)	10	4.96	2.228	4.96
(1,14)	14	4.60	2.145	4.60
(1,20)	20	4.35	2.086	4.35

The F-distribution with (1,k) degrees of freedom is the same as a t^2-distribution where t has k degrees of freedom.

10.64 $\bar{x}_A = 666/16 = 41.63$

$$s_A^2 = \frac{16(29572) - (666)^2}{(16)(15)} = 123.32$$

$\bar{x}_B = 415/14 = 29.64$

$$s_B^2 = \frac{14(12467) - (415)^2}{(14)(13)} = 12.71$$

(a) $H_0: \sigma_A^2 = \sigma_B^2$ $H_a: \sigma_A^2 \neq \sigma_B^2$ $\alpha = 0.05$

Observed value: $F = 123.32/12.71 = 9.7,$ df = (15,13)

Critical value: $F = 3.05$. Decision: reject H_0.

Assume $\sigma_A^2 \neq \sigma_B^2$

$H_0: \mu_A - \mu_B \leq 0$ $H_a: \mu_A - \mu_B > 0$ $\alpha = 0.05$

Observed value: $t = \dfrac{(41.63 - 29.64) - 0}{\sqrt{\dfrac{123.32}{16} + \dfrac{12.71}{14}}} = 4.08,$ df = 13.

Critical value: $t = 1.771$. Decision: reject H_0. There is sufficient evidence to support the engineer's suspicion.

(b) $(41.63 - 29.64) \pm (1.771) \sqrt{\dfrac{123.32}{16} + \dfrac{12.71}{14}}$

   or $6.79 < \mu_A - \mu_B < 17.19$.

11.1   (a) $b_0 = 4$, $b_1 = 7$

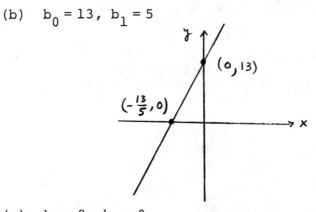

(b) $b_0 = 13$, $b_1 = 5$

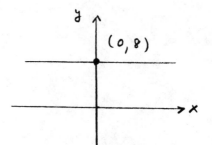

(c) $b_0 = 8$, $b_1 = 0$

11.1   (d) $b_0 = 9/2$, $b_1 = -2$

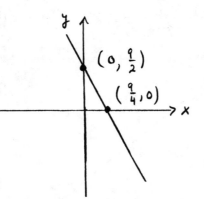

(e) $b_0 = 4$, $b_1 = 3$

11.2 $\sum x = 24$ $\sum y = 30$ $\sum xy = 96$ $\sum x^2 = 112$ n=6 $\bar{x}=4$ $\bar{y}=5$

$b_1 = \dfrac{6(96) - (24)(30)}{6(112) - (24)^2} = -1.5$ $b_0 = 5 - (-1.5)4 = 11$ $\hat{y}=11-1.5x$

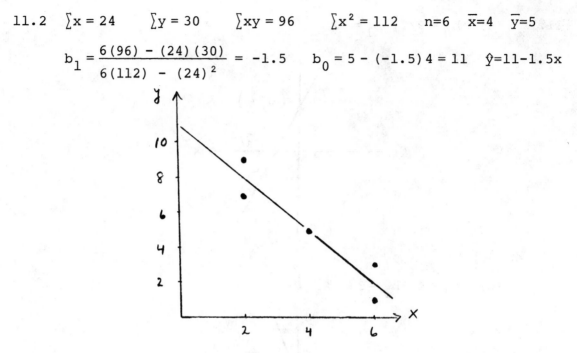

11.3 $\sum x = 7$ $\sum y = 42$ $\sum xy = 54$ $\sum x^2 = 13$ n = 7 $\bar{x} = 1$ $\bar{y} = 6$

$b_1 = \dfrac{7(54) - (7)(42)}{7(13) - (7)^2} = 2$ $b_0 = 6 - (2)(1) = 4$ $\hat{y} = 4 + 2x$

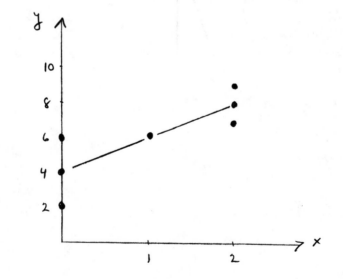

11.4 $\sum x = 5$ $\sum y = 15$ $\sum xy = 9$ $\sum x^2 = 9$ $n = 5$ $\bar{x} = 1$ $\bar{y} = 3$

$b_1 = \dfrac{5(9) - (5)(15)}{5(9) - (5)^2} = -1.5$ $b_0 = 3 - (-1.5)(1) = 4.5$

$\hat{y} = 4.5 - 1.5x$

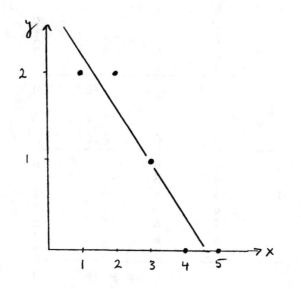

11.5 $\sum x = 15$ $\sum y = 5$ $\sum xy = 9$ $\sum x^2 = 55$ $n = 5$ $\bar{x} = 3$ $\bar{y} = 1$

$b_1 = \dfrac{5(9) - (15)(5)}{5(55) - (15)^2} = -0.6$ $b_0 = 1 - (-0.6)(3) = 2.8$ $\hat{y} = 2.8 - 0.6x$

169

11.6 $\sum x = 12$ $\sum y = 40$ $\sum xy = 160$ $\sum x^2 = 46$ $n = 4$ $\bar{x} = 3$ $\bar{y} = 10$

$b_1 = \dfrac{4(160) - (12)(40)}{4(46) - (12)^2} = 4$ $b_0 = 10 - (4)(3) = -2$ $\hat{y} = -2 + 4x$

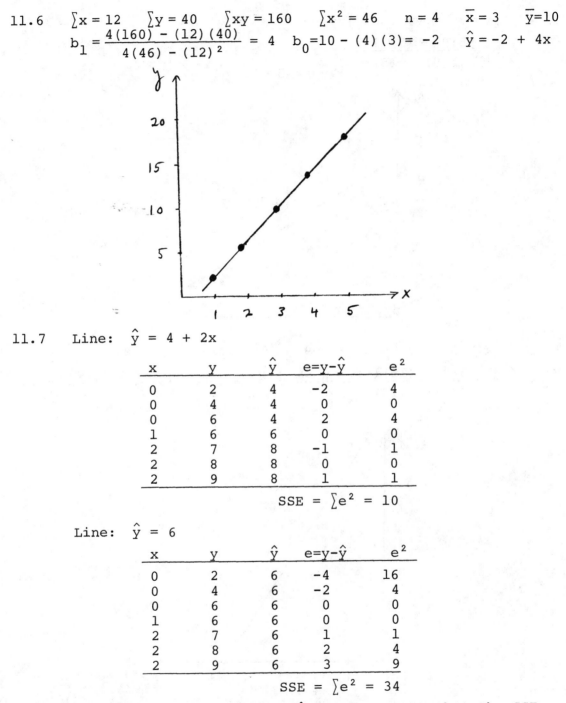

11.7   Line: $\hat{y} = 4 + 2x$

x	y	$\hat{y}$	$e = y - \hat{y}$	e^2
0	2	4	-2	4
0	4	4	0	0
0	6	4	2	4
1	6	6	0	0
2	7	8	-1	1
2	8	8	0	0
2	9	8	1	1

$$\text{SSE} = \sum e^2 = 10$$

Line: $\hat{y} = 6$

x	y	$\hat{y}$	$e = y - \hat{y}$	e^2
0	2	6	-4	16
0	4	6	-2	4
0	6	6	0	0
1	6	6	0	0
2	7	6	1	1
2	8	6	2	4
2	9	6	3	9

$$\text{SSE} = \sum e^2 = 34$$

The line of best fit is given by $\hat{y} = 4 + 2x$. Note that the SSE computed from $\hat{y} = 4 + 2x$ is smaller than the SSE computed from $\hat{y} = 6$.

11.8

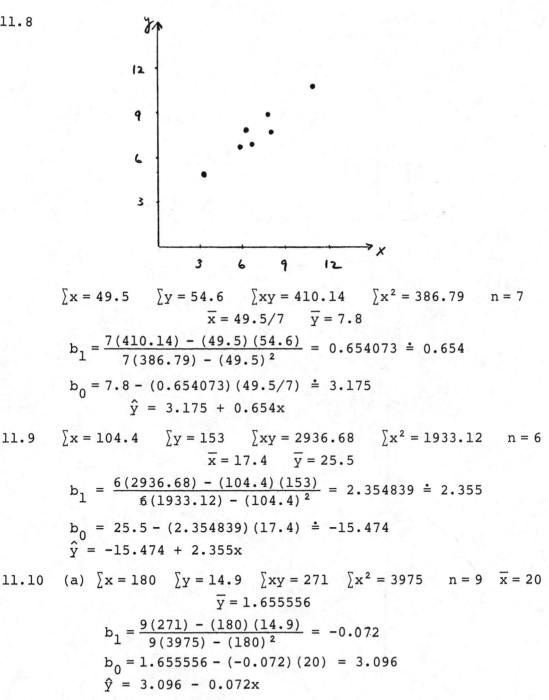

$\sum x = 49.5$ $\sum y = 54.6$ $\sum xy = 410.14$ $\sum x^2 = 386.79$ $n = 7$

$\bar{x} = 49.5/7$ $\bar{y} = 7.8$

$b_1 = \dfrac{7(410.14) - (49.5)(54.6)}{7(386.79) - (49.5)^2} = 0.654073 \doteq 0.654$

$b_0 = 7.8 - (0.654073)(49.5/7) \doteq 3.175$

$\hat{y} = 3.175 + 0.654x$

11.9 $\sum x = 104.4$ $\sum y = 153$ $\sum xy = 2936.68$ $\sum x^2 = 1933.12$ $n = 6$

$\bar{x} = 17.4$ $\bar{y} = 25.5$

$b_1 = \dfrac{6(2936.68) - (104.4)(153)}{6(1933.12) - (104.4)^2} = 2.354839 \doteq 2.355$

$b_0 = 25.5 - (2.354839)(17.4) \doteq -15.474$

$\hat{y} = -15.474 + 2.355x$

11.10   (a) $\sum x = 180$ $\sum y = 14.9$ $\sum xy = 271$ $\sum x^2 = 3975$ $n = 9$ $\bar{x} = 20$

$\bar{y} = 1.655556$

$b_1 = \dfrac{9(271) - (180)(14.9)}{9(3975) - (180)^2} = -0.072$

$b_0 = 1.655556 - (-0.072)(20) = 3.096$

$\hat{y} = 3.096 - 0.072x$

171

11.10 (a) Continued:

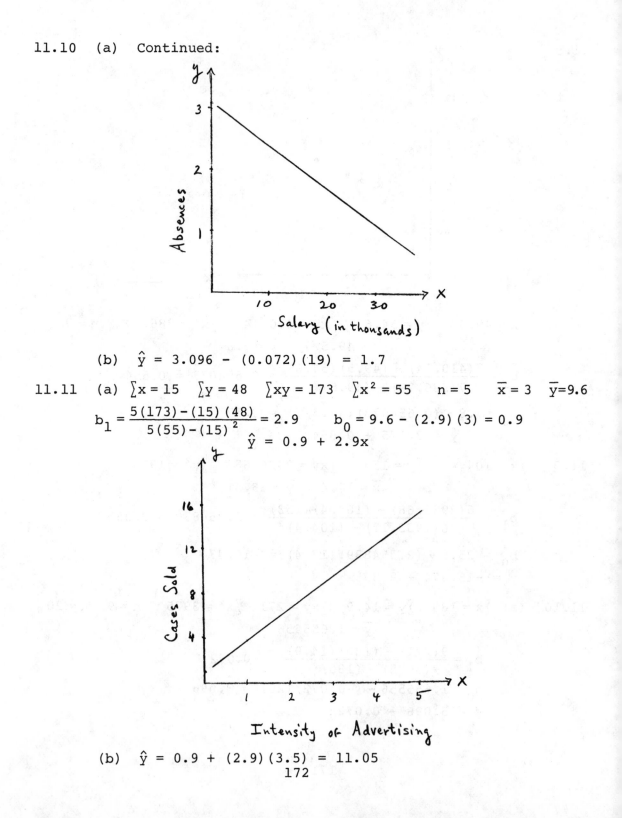

(b) $\hat{y} = 3.096 - (0.072)(19) = 1.7$

11.11 (a) $\sum x = 15$ $\sum y = 48$ $\sum xy = 173$ $\sum x^2 = 55$ $n = 5$ $\bar{x} = 3$ $\bar{y} = 9.6$

$b_1 = \dfrac{5(173) - (15)(48)}{5(55) - (15)^2} = 2.9$ $b_0 = 9.6 - (2.9)(3) = 0.9$

$\hat{y} = 0.9 + 2.9x$

(b) $\hat{y} = 0.9 + (2.9)(3.5) = 11.05$

11.12 $\sum x = 71$ $\sum y = 54.6$ $\sum xy = 509.8$ $\sum x^2 = 919$ $n = 7$

$\bar{x} = 71/7$ $\bar{y} = 7.8$

$b_1 = \dfrac{7(509.8) - (71)(54.6)}{7(919) - (71)^2} = -0.221264 \doteq -0.221$

$b_0 = 7.8 - (-0.221264)(71/7) = 10.044$

$\hat{y} = 10.044 - 0.221x$

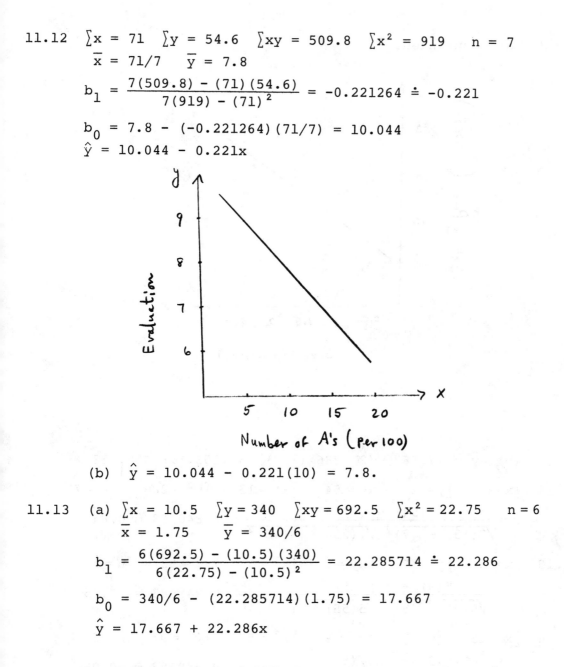

Number of A's (per 100)

(b) $\hat{y} = 10.044 - 0.221(10) = 7.8$.

11.13 (a) $\sum x = 10.5$ $\sum y = 340$ $\sum xy = 692.5$ $\sum x^2 = 22.75$ $n = 6$

$\bar{x} = 1.75$ $\bar{y} = 340/6$

$b_1 = \dfrac{6(692.5) - (10.5)(340)}{6(22.75) - (10.5)^2} = 22.285714 \doteq 22.286$

$b_0 = 340/6 - (22.285714)(1.75) = 17.667$

$\hat{y} = 17.667 + 22.286x$

11.13 (a) Continued:

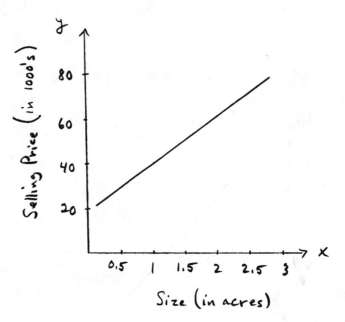

(b) $\hat{y} = 17.667 + (22.286)(1.7) = 55.553$, or \$55,553

11.14 $\sum x = 7$ $\sum y = 42$ $\sum xy = 54$ $\sum x^2 = 13$ $\sum y^2 = 286$ $n = 7$

$$r = \frac{7(54) - (7)(42)}{\sqrt{7(13) - (7)^2} \ \sqrt{7(286) - (42)^2}} = 0.840168 \doteq 0.84$$

11.15 $\sum x = 5$ $\sum y = 15$ $\sum xy = 9$ $\sum x^2 = 9$ $\sum y^2 = 55$ $n = 5$

$$r = \frac{5(9) - (5)(15)}{\sqrt{5(9) - (5)^2} \ \sqrt{5(55) - (15)^2}} = -0.948683 \doteq -0.95$$

11.16 $\sum x = 15$ $\sum y = 5$ $\sum xy = 9$ $\sum x^2 = 55$ $\sum y^2 = 9$ $n = 5$

$$r = \frac{5(9) - (15)(5)}{\sqrt{5(55) - (15)^2} \ \sqrt{5(9) - (5)^2}} = -0.948683 \doteq -0.95$$

11.17 $\sum x = 12$ $\sum y = 40$ $\sum xy = 160$ $\sum x^2 = 46$ $\sum y^2 = 560$ $n = 4$

$$r = \frac{4(160) - (12)(40)}{\sqrt{4(46) - (12)^2}\,\sqrt{4(560) - (40)^2}} = 1$$

11.18 (a) $\sum x = 104.4$ $\sum y = 153$ $\sum xy = 2936.68$ $\sum x^2 = 1933.12$
$\sum y^2 = 4586.66$ $n = 6$

$$r = \frac{6(2936.68) - (104.4)(153)}{\sqrt{6(1933.12) - (104.4)^2}\,\sqrt{6(4586.66) - (153)^2}} = 0.97127$$

$r^2 = 0.943$

Approximately 94.3% of the variation in mortality rate per 100000 of Canadian males is explained by cigarette consumption.

(b) $\sum x = 10.5$ $\sum y = 340$ $\sum xy = 692.5$ $\sum x^2 = 22.75$
$\sum y^2 = 21500$ $n = 6$

$$r = \frac{6(692.5) - (10.5)(340)}{\sqrt{6(22.75) - (10.5)^2}\,\sqrt{6(21500) - (340)^2}} = 0.986368$$

$r^2 = 0.973$

Approximately 97.3% of the variation in selling price is explained by size of land.

11.19 From exercise 11.11, $\hat{y} = 0.9 + 2.9x$ and $\bar{y} = 9.6$.

(a)

y	$\hat{y}$	$\bar{y}$	$(y-\bar{y})^2$	$(\hat{y}-\bar{y})^2$
4	3.8	9.6	31.36	33.64
7	6.7	9.6	6.76	8.41
8	9.6	9.6	2.56	0
14	12.5	9.6	19.36	8.41
15	15.4	9.6	29.16	33.64
Sums:			89.2	84.1

(i) TSS = 89.2   (ii) SSR = 84.1

$r^2 = \text{SSR/TSS} = 84.1/89.2 = 0.943$

(b) $\sum x = 15$ $\sum y = 48$ $\sum xy = 173$ $\sum x^2 = 55$ $\sum y^2 = 550$ $n = 5$

$$r = \frac{5(173) - (15)(48)}{\sqrt{5(55) - (15)^2}\,\sqrt{5(550) - (48)^2}} = 0.970992$$

$r^2 = 0.943$

11.20 (a) TSS = SSR + SSE = 40 + 60 = 100 r^2=SSR/TSS = 40/100 = 2/5

(b) SSE = TSS - SSR=300-100 = 200 r^2=SSR/TSS=100/300= 1/3

(c) SSR = TSS - SSE = 50 - 20 = 30 r^2=SSR/TSS = 30/50 = 3/5

(d) TSS = SSR/r^2=80/0.4 = 200   SSE = TSS - SSR = 200 - 80 = 120

(e) 1-r^2=SSE/TSS, so TSS=SSE/(1-r^2)=27/0.3 = 90
    SSR = TSS - SSE = 90 - 27 = 63

(f) SSR = (TSS)r^2 = (40)(0.2) = 8   SSE = TSS-SSR = 40-8 = 32

(g) TSS = SSR/r^2 = 25/1 = 25   SSE = TSS - SSR = 25 - 25 = 0

(h) TSS = SSR + SSE = 30+0 = 30 r^2 = SSR/TSS = 30/30 = 1

11.21 (a) $s_x^2 = \dfrac{n\sum x^2 - (\sum x)^2}{n(n-1)} = \dfrac{5(63) - (15)^2}{(5)(4)} = 4.5,$

so $s_x = \sqrt{4.5} = 2.121$

$s_y^2 = \dfrac{(5)(114) - (20)^2}{(5)(4)} = 8.5,$ so $s_y = \sqrt{8.5} = 2.915$

$\sum x = 15$ $\sum y = 20$ $\sum xy=77$ $\sum x^2 = 63$ $\sum y^2=114$ n=5

$\bar{x} = 3$ $\bar{y} = 4$

(b) $r = \dfrac{5(77) - (15)(20)}{\sqrt{5(63)-(15)^2}\sqrt{5(114)-(20)^2}} = 0.687184 \doteq 0.687$

(c) $b_1 = \dfrac{5(77) - (15)(20)}{\sqrt{5(63) - (15)^2}} = 0.944444 \doteq 0.944$

$b_0 = 4 - (0.944444)(3) \doteq 1.167$

$\hat{y} = 1.167 + 0.944x$

11.22 $H_0: \rho = 0$ $H_a: \rho \neq 0$ $\alpha = 0.01$

Observed value: r = 0.84 (from exercise 11.14)
Critical values: r = +0.875. Decision: fail to reject H_0.

11.23 $\sum x=12$ $\sum y=12$ $\sum xy=34$ $\sum x^2=56$ $\sum y^2=50$ n = 4

$H_0: \rho = 0$ $H_a: \rho \neq 0$ $\alpha = 0.05$

Observed value: $r = \dfrac{4(34) - (12)(12)}{\sqrt{4(56)-(12)^2}\sqrt{4(50)-(12)^2}} = -0.119523$
$\doteq -0.12$

Critical values: r = +0.95. Decision: fail to reject H_0.

11.24 H_0: $\rho = 0$ H_a: $\rho \neq 0$ $\alpha = 0.05$
Observed value: r = -0.95 (from exercise 11.15)
Critical values: r = ±0.878. Decision: reject H_0.

11.25 H_0: $\rho = 0$ H_a: $\rho \neq 0$ $\alpha = 0.05$
Observed value: r = -0.95 (from exercise 11.16)
Critical values: r = ± 0.878. Decision: reject H_0.

11.26 H_0: $\rho = 0$ H_a: $\rho \neq 0$ $\alpha = 0.05$
Observed value: r = 1 (from exercise 11.17)
Critical values: r = ±0.95. Decision: reject H_0.

11.27 $\sum x = 10.4$ $\sum y = 51.2$ $\sum xy = 89.77$ $\sum x^2 = 18.42$ $\sum y^2 = 442.6$
$$n = 6$$

H_0: $\rho = 0$ H_a: $\rho \neq 0$ $\alpha = 0.05$

Observed value: $r = \dfrac{6(89.77) - (10.4)(51.2)}{\sqrt{6(18.42)-(10.4)^2}\sqrt{6(442.6)-(51.2)^2}}$

$= 0.683838 \doteq 0.68$

Critical values: r = ±0.811. Decision: fail to reject H_0.
The data do not indicate a linear relationship between
sales of passenger cars for imports and domestic.

11.28 $\sum x = 20.2$ $\sum y = 562$ $\sum xy = 1668.5$ $\sum x^2 = 60.1$ $\sum y^2 = 46424$ n=7
$$\bar{x} = 2.885714 \qquad \bar{y} = 80.285714$$

(a) H_0: $\rho = 0$ H_a: $\rho \neq 0$ $\alpha = 0.05$
Observed value:

$r = \dfrac{7(1668.5) - (20.2)(562)}{\sqrt{7(60.1) - (20.2)^2}\ \sqrt{7(46424) - (562)^2}}$

$= 0.962434 \doteq 0.96$

Critical values: r = ±0.754. Decision: reject H_0.
The data indicate a linear relationship between
grade-point average and final grade.

(b) $b_1 = \dfrac{7(1668.5)-(20.2)(562)}{7(60.1) - (20.2)^2} = 25.837283 \doteq 25.837$

$b_0 = 80.285714 - (25.837283)(2.885714) = 5.727$

$$\hat{y} = 5.727 + 25.837x$$

(c) $\hat{y} = 5.727 + (25.837)(2.5) \doteq 70$

11.29 $\sum x=1280$ $\sum y=104$ $\sum xy=18745$ $\sum x^2=237100$ $\sum y^2=1526$ $n=8$
$\bar{x}=160$ $\bar{y}=13$

(a) $H_0: \rho = 0$ $H_a: \rho \neq 0$ $\alpha = 0.01$

Observed value:

$$r= \frac{8(18745) - (1280)(104)}{\sqrt{8(237100) - (1280)^2} \ \sqrt{8(1526) - (104)^2}} = 0.887925 \doteq 0.89$$

Critical values: $r = \pm 0.834$. Decision: reject H_0. The data indicate a linear relationship between population and number of courts.

(b) $b_1 = \frac{8(18745)-(1280)(104)}{8(237100) - (1280)^2} = 0.06517 \doteq 0.065$

$b_0 = 13 - (0.06517)(160) = 2.572755 \doteq 2.573$

$\hat{y} = 2.573 + 0.065x$

(c) $\hat{y} = 2.573 + (0.065)(135) \doteq 11$

11.30 $\sum x=96$ $\sum y=59$ $\sum xy=881$ $\sum x^2=2062$ $\sum y^2=491$ $n=8$

$H_0: \rho = 0$ $H_a: \rho \neq 0$ $\alpha = 0.01$

Observed value:

$$r = \frac{8(881) - (96)(59)}{\sqrt{8(2062) - (96)^2} \ \sqrt{8(491) - (59)^2}} = 0.767214 \doteq 0.77$$

Critical values: $r = \pm 0.834$. Decision: fail to reject H_0. The data do not indicate a linear relationship between percent sugars and cost per serving.

11.31 $\sum x=25$ $\sum y=40$ $\sum xy=176$ $\sum x^2=145$ $\sum y^2=350$ $n=5$ $\bar{x}=5$ $\bar{y}=8$

(a) $H_0: \rho = 0$ $H_a: \rho \neq 0$ $\alpha = 0.05$

Observed value:

$$r = \frac{5(176) - (25)(40)}{\sqrt{5(145) - (25)^2} \ \sqrt{5(350) - (40)^2}} = -0.98$$

Critical values: $r = \pm 0.878$. Decision: reject H_0.

(b) $b_1 = \frac{5(176)-(25)(40)}{5(145) - (25)^2} = -1.2$ $b_0 = 8 - (-1.2)5 = 14$

$\hat{y} = 14 - 1.2x$

(c) $\hat{y} = 14 - (1.2)(7) = 5.6$

11.31 (d)

x	y	$\hat{y}$	$y-\hat{y}$	$(y-\hat{y})^2$
2	12	11.6	0.4	0.16
4	9	9.2	-0.2	0.04
5	8	8	0	0
6	6	6.8	-0.8	0.64
8	5	4.4	0.6	0.36
				1.2 = SSE

$S = \sqrt{1.2/(5-2)} = 0.63$ df $= 5-2 = 3$ $t(0.025) = 3.182$

$$x_0 = 7 \qquad \hat{y}_0 = 5.6$$

$$5.6 \pm (3.182)(0.63)\sqrt{1 + \frac{1}{5} + \frac{(7-5)^2}{145 - (25)^2/5}}$$

or 3.23 to 7.97

11.32 $\sum x=49$ $\sum y=40$ $\sum xy=335$ $\sum x^2=437$ $\sum y^2=280$ n=7 $\bar{x}=7$ $\bar{y}=40/7$

(a) $H_0: \rho = 0$ $H_a: \rho \neq 0$ $\alpha = 0.05$

Observed value:
$$r = \frac{7(335) - (49)(40)}{\sqrt{7(437) - (49)^2}\ \sqrt{7(280) - (40)^2}} \doteq 0.79$$

Critical values: $r = \pm 0.754$. Decision: reject H_0.

(b) $b_1 = \dfrac{7(335) - (49)(40)}{7(437) - (49)^2} = 0.585106 \doteq 0.585$

$b_0 = 40/7 - (0.585106)(7) = 1.618541 \doteq 1.619$

$$\hat{y} = 1.619 + 0.585x$$

(c) $\hat{y} = 1.619 + (0.585)(5) = 4.54$

(d)

x	y	$\hat{y}$	$y-\hat{y}$	$(y-\hat{y})^2$
4	2	3.959	-1.959	3.838
4	2	3.959	-1.959	3.838
4	5	3.959	1.041	1.084
6	6	5.129	0.871	0.759
8	7	6.299	0.701	0.491
8	9	6.299	2.701	7.295
15	9	10.394	-1.394	1.943
				19.248 = SSE

$S = \sqrt{19.248/(7-2)} = 1.96$ df$=7-2=5$ $t(0.025)=2.571$

$$x_0 = 5 \qquad \hat{y}_0 = 4.544$$

$$4.54 \pm (2.571)(1.96)\sqrt{1 + \frac{1}{7} + \frac{(5-7)^2}{437 - (49)^2/7}} \text{ or } -0.95 \text{ to } 10.03.$$

179

11.33　(a)　From exercise 11.28, $\hat{y} = 5.727 + 25.837x$　　$\bar{x} = 2.89$

$\sum x^2 = 60.1$　　$\sum x = 20.2$　　$n = 7$

Now SSE = 96.089.　$S = \sqrt{96.089/(7-2)} = 4.38$

df = 7 - 2 = 5　　t(0.025) = 2.571　　$x_0 = 2.5$

$\hat{y}_0 = 5.727 + (25.837)(2.5) = 70.32$

$70.32 \pm (2.571)(4.38)\sqrt{1 + \dfrac{1}{7} + \dfrac{(2.5 - 2.89)^2}{60.1 - (20.2)^2/7}}$

or 57.86 to 82.78.

(b)　From exercise 11.29, $\hat{y} = 2.573 + 0.065x$　　$\bar{x} = 160$

$\sum x^2 = 237100$　　$\sum x = 1280$　　$n = 8$.

Now SSE = 36.823.

$S = \sqrt{36.823/(8-2)} = 2.48$　　df = 8 - 2 = 6　　t(0.05) = 1.943

$x_0 = 200$　　$\hat{y}_0 = 2.573 + (0.065)(200) = 15.57$

$15.57 \pm (1.943)(2.48)\sqrt{1 + \dfrac{1}{8} + \dfrac{(200 - 160)^2}{237100 - (1280)^2/8}}$

or 10.35 to 20.79.

11.34　$\sum x = 25$　$\sum y = 20$　$\sum xy = 85$　$\sum x^2 = 143$　$n = 5$　$\bar{x} = 5$　$\bar{y} = 4$

(a)　$b_1 = \dfrac{5(85) - (25)(20)}{5(143) - (25)^2} = -0.833333 \doteq -0.83$

$b_0 = 4 - (-0.833333)(5) = 8.17$　　　$\hat{y} = 8.17 - 0.83x$

(b)

x	y	$\hat{y}$	$y - \hat{y}$	$(y-\hat{y})^2$
3	7	5.68	1.32	1.7424
3	5	5.68	-0.68	0.4624
5	3	4.02	-1.02	1.0404
6	3	3.19	-0.19	0.0361
8	2	1.53	0.47	0.2209
				3.5022 = SSE

(c)

x	y	$\hat{y}$	$y - \hat{y}$	$(y-\hat{y})^2$
3	7	4	3	9
3	5	4	1	1
5	3	4	-1	1
6	3	4	-1	1
8	2	4	-2	4
				16 = SSE

(d)　The line of best fit minimizes SSE.

11.35 (a) (1,1) (2,2) (3,3) (4,4)

(b) (1,-1) (2,-2) (3,-3) (4,-4)

(c) (1,0) (1,1) (1,-1) (-1,0)

11.36 (a) $\sum x=30$ $\sum y=18$ $\sum xy=105$ $\sum x^2=162$ $n=6$ $\bar{x}=5$ $\bar{y}=3$

$$b_1 = \frac{6(105)-(30)(18)}{6(162)-(30)^2} = 1.25 \qquad b_0 = 3-(1.25)(5) = -3.25$$

$$\hat{y} = -3.25 + 1.25x$$

(b)
y	$\hat{y}$	$\bar{y}$	$(y-\bar{y})^2$	$(\hat{y}-\bar{y})^2$
0	-0.75	3	9	14.0625
0	3	3	9	0
3	3	3	0	0
4	4.25	3	1	1.5625
4	4.25	3	1	1.5625
7	4.25	3	16	1.5625
			36	18.75

(c) TSS = 36 SSR = 18.75

(d) $r^2 = 18.75/36 = 0.52$. So 52% of the variation in y is explained by x.

11.37 (a) TSS=SSR + SSE=50 + 50=100 r^2=SSR/TSS=50/100=0.5

(b) SSE=TSS - SSR=400 - 100=300 r^2=SSR/TSS=100/400=0.25

(c) SSR=TSS - SSE=50 - 40=10 r^2=SSR/TSS=10/50=0.2

(d) TSS=SSR/r^2=90/0.6=150 SSE=TSS-SSR=150-90=60

(e) TSS=SSE/$(1 - r^2)$=28/0.7=40 SSR=TSS-SSE=40-28=12

(f) SSR=r^2(TSS)=(0.8)(40)=32 SSE=TSS-SSR=40-32=8

(g) TSS=SSR/r^2=50/1=50 SSE=TSS-SSR=50-50=0

(h) SSR=TSS - SSE=75 - 0=75 r^2=SSR/TSS=75/75=1

11.38 $\sum x=49.5$ $\sum y=54.6$ $\sum xy=410.04$ $\sum x^2=386.79$ $\sum y^2=444.94$ $n=7$

(a) $$r=\frac{7(410.04) - (49.5)(54.6)}{\sqrt{7(386.79)-(49.5)^2} \ \sqrt{7(444.94)-(54.6)^2}} = 0.91$$

(b) H_0: $\rho = 0$ H_a: $\rho \neq 0$ $\alpha = 0.05$
Observed value: r=0.91. Critical values: r=+0.754
Decision: reject H_0. The data indicate a linear
relationship between inflation rate and prime lending
rate.

(c) $\hat{y} = 3.175 + (0.654)(7) = 7.75$

11.39 $\sum x = 104.4$ $\sum y = 153$ $\sum xy = 2936.68$ $\sum x^2 = 1933.12$
$\sum y^2 = 4586.66$ $n = 6$

(a) $r = \dfrac{6(2936.68) - (104.4)(153)}{\sqrt{6(1933.12) - (104.4)^2}\ \sqrt{6(4586.66) - (153)^2}} = 0.97$

(b) $H_0: \rho = 0$ $\qquad$ $H_a: \rho \neq 0$ $\qquad$ $\alpha = 0.01$

Observed value: $r = 0.97$. Critical values: $r = \pm 0.917$

Decision: reject H_0. The data indicate a linear relationship between cigarette consumption and mortality rate.

(c) $\hat{y} = -15.474 + (2.355)(20) = 31.6$ (per 100,000).

11.40 (a) $\sum x = 26.9$ $\sum y = 123.6$ $\sum xy = 272.42$ $\sum x^2 = 61.69$ $\sum y^2 = 1323.08$
$n = 12$

$r = \dfrac{12(272.42) - (26.9)(123.6)}{\sqrt{12(61.69) - (26.9)^2}\ \sqrt{12(1323.08) - (123.6)^2}} = -0.56$

(b) $H_0: \rho = 0$ $\qquad$ $H_a: \rho \neq 0$ $\qquad$ $\alpha = 0.05$

Observed value: $r = -0.56$. Critical values: $r = \pm 0.576$.

Decision: fail to reject H_0. The data do not indicate a linear relationship between numbers of Ph.D.'s in mathematics and statistics.

11.41 (a) $\sum x = 56$ $\sum y = 56$ $\sum xy = 473.3$ $\sum x^2 = 598$ $\sum y^2 = 460.08$ $n = 7$

$r = \dfrac{7(473.3) - (56)(56)}{\sqrt{7(598) - (56)^2}\ \sqrt{7(460.08) - (56)^2}} = 0.59$

(b) $H_0: \rho = 0$ $\qquad$ $H_a: \rho \neq 0$ $\qquad$ $\alpha = 0.05$
Observed value: $r = 0.59$. Critical values: $r = \pm 0.754$.

Decision: fail to reject H_0. The data do not indicate a linear relationship between years of teaching and effectiveness rating.

11.42 $\sum x=174$ $\sum y=218$ $\sum xy=7901$ $\sum x^2=6136$ $\sum y^2=11056$ $n = 7$

$\bar{x} = 24.857143$ $\bar{y} = 31.142857$

(a) $r = \dfrac{7(7901) - (174)(218)}{\sqrt{7(6136)-(174)^2} \; \sqrt{7(11056)-(218)^2}} = 0.89$

(b) H_0: $\rho = 0$ H_a: $\rho \neq 0$ $\alpha = 0.05$

Observed value: $r = 0.89$.   Critical values: $r = \pm 0.754$.

Decision: reject H_0.   The data indicate a linear relationship between cholesterol intake and death rate.

(c) $b_1 = \dfrac{7(7901) - (174)(218)}{7(6136) - (174)^2} = 1.370701 \doteq 1.37$

$b_0 = 31.142857 - (1.370701)(24.857143) = -2.93.$

     $\hat{y} = -2.93 + 1.37x$

(d) $\hat{y} = -2.93 + (1.37)(40) = 51.87$ (per million).

11.43 $\sum x=460$ $\sum y=120$ $\sum xy=8942$ $\sum x^2=35694$ $\sum y^2=2594$ $n = 6$

$\bar{x} = 460/6$ $\bar{y} = 20$

(a) $r = \dfrac{6(8942) - (460)(120)}{\sqrt{6(35694)-(460)^2} \; \sqrt{6(2594)-(120)^2}} = -0.896$

(b) H_0: $\rho = 0$ H_a: $\rho \neq 0$ $\alpha = 0.05$

Observed value: $r = -0.896$.   Critical values: $r = \pm 0.811$.

Decision: reject H_0.   The data indicate a linear relationship between temperature and number of customers.

(c) $b_1 = \dfrac{6(8942) - (460)(120)}{6(35694) - (460)^2} = -0.603744 \doteq -0.60$

$b_0 = 20 - (-0.603744)(460/6) = 66.29.$

$\hat{y} = 66.29 - 0.6x.$

11.43 (c) Continued:

(d) $\hat{y} = 66.29 - (0.6)(70) \doteq 24.$

11.44 (a) $\sum x = 597$ $\sum y = 4711$ $\sum xy = 353091$ $\sum x^2 = 44637$ $\sum y^2 = 2857463$

n = 8

$$r = \frac{8(353091) - (597)(4711)}{\sqrt{8(44637) - (597)^2} \sqrt{8(2857463) - (4711)^2}} = 0.57$$

(b) $H_0: \rho = 0$ $H_a: \rho \neq 0$ $\alpha = 0.01$

Observed value: $r = 0.57$. Critical values: $r = \pm0.834$. Decision: fail to reject H_0. The data do not indicate a linear relationship between rating and price.

11.45 $\sum x = 25.4$ $\sum y = 279$ $\sum xy = 925$ $\sum x^2 = 89.06$ $\sum y^2 = 9925$ n = 8

$\overline{x} = 3.175$ $\overline{y} = 34.875$

(a) $$r = \frac{8(925) - (25.4)(279)}{\sqrt{8(89.06) - (25.4)^2} \sqrt{8(9925) - (279)^2}} = 0.97$$

11.45   (b) $H_0: \rho = 0$ $H_a: \rho \neq 0$ $\alpha = 0.01$

          Observed value: $r = 0.97$.   Critical values: $r = \pm 0.834$.

          Decision: reject H_0.   The data indicate a linear relationship between pounds of fertilizer and bushels of soybeans.

    (c) $b_1 = \dfrac{8(925) - (25.4)(279)}{8(89.06) - (25.4)^2} = 4.655377 \doteq 4.66$

        $b_0 = 34.875 - (4.655377)(3.175) = 20.09$

            $\hat{y} = 20.09 + 4.66x$

Pounds (hundreds per acre)

    (d) $\hat{y} = 20.09 + (4.66)(3.5) = 36.4$.

11.46 $\sum x = 12$ $\sum y = 28$ $\sum xy = 37.56$ $\sum x^2 = 26.18$ $\sum y^2 = 101.14$ $n = 8$

     $\overline{x} = 1.5$ $\overline{y} = 3.5$

    (a)

      $r = \dfrac{8(37.56) - (12)(28)}{\sqrt{8(26.18) - (12)^2} \ \sqrt{8(101.14) - (28)^2}} = -0.88$

11.46 (b) $H_0: \rho = 0$ $H_a: \rho \neq 0$ $\alpha = 0.05$
Observed value: $r = -0.88$. Critical values:
$$r = \pm 0.707.$$

Decision: reject H_0. The data indicate a linear relationship between distance from a rapid transit station and rent.

(c) $b_1 = \dfrac{8(37.56) - (12)(28)}{8(26.18) - (12)^2} = -0.542787 \doteq -0.54$

$b_0 = 3.5 - (-0.542787)(1.5) = 4.31$

$\hat{y} = 4.31 - 0.54x$

(d) $\hat{y} = 4.31 - (0.54)(1.5) = 3.5$, or $350.

11.47 (a) From exercise 11.43, $\hat{y} = 66.29 - 0.6x$. $\bar{x} = 76.67$.
$\sum x^2 = 35694$ $\sum x = 460$ $n = 6$. Now SSE = 38.7446.
$S = \sqrt{38.7446/(6 - 2)} = 3.11$ df=6-2=4 $t(0.005)=4.604$.
$x_0 = 70$ $\hat{y}_0 = 66.29 - (0.6)(70) = 24.29$.

$24.29 \pm (4.604)(3.11)\sqrt{1 + \dfrac{1}{6} + \dfrac{(70 - 76.67)^2}{35694 - (460)^2/6}}$

or 8.15 to 40.43 or 8 to 40 customers.

(b) From exercise 11.45, $\hat{y} = 20.09 + 4.66x$ $\bar{x} = 3.175$
$\sum x^2 = 89.06$ $\sum x = 25.4$ $n=8$. Now SSE = 12.501656.
$S = \sqrt{12.501656/(8 - 2)} = 1.44$ df=8-2=6
$$t(0.025) = 2.447$$
$x_0 = 3.5$ $\hat{y}_0 = 20.09 + (4.66)(3.5) = 36.4$

$36.4 \pm (2.447)(1.44)\sqrt{1 + \dfrac{1}{8} + \dfrac{(3.5 - 3.175)^2}{89.06 - (25.4)^2/8}}$

or 32.64 to 40.16.

(c) From exercise 11.46, $\hat{y} = 4.31 - 0.54x$ $\bar{x} = 1.5$
$\sum x^2 = 26.18$ $\sum x = 12$ $n=8$. Now SSE = 0.730088.
$S = \sqrt{0.730088/(8 - 2)} = 0.35$ df = 8-2=6 $t(0.025)=2.447$
$x_0 = 1.5$ $\hat{y}_0 = 4.31 - (0.54)(1.5) = 3.5$

$3.5 \pm (2.447)(0.35)\sqrt{1 + \dfrac{1}{8} + \dfrac{(1.5 - 1.5)^2}{26.18 - (12)^2/8}}$ or 2.59 to 4.41.

12.1

	Observed F	F(α)	df	Decision
(a)	$\dfrac{5(50)}{(100/3)} = 7.5$	3.89	(2,12)	Reject H_0
(b)	$\dfrac{5(20)}{(100/3)} = 3$	3.89	(2,12)	Fail to reject H_0
(c)	$\dfrac{6(25)}{(50/2)} = 6$	10.04	(1,10)	Fail to reject H_0
(d)	$\dfrac{6(25)}{(25/2)} = 12$	10.04	(1,10)	Reject H_0
(e)	$\dfrac{4(40)}{(200/5)} = 4$	3.06	(4,15)	Reject H_0
(f)	$\dfrac{4(40)}{(400/5)} = 2$	3.06	(4,15)	Fail to reject H_0

12.2 H_0: $\mu_A = \mu_B = \mu_C = \mu_D = \mu_E = \mu_F$

H_a: Not all the means are equal.

$\alpha = 0.05$ df $= (5,18)$ Critical value: F $= 2.77$

	Observed value	Decision
(a)	$F = \dfrac{4(5)}{(40/6)} = 3$	Reject H_0
(b)	$F = \dfrac{4(4)}{(40/6)} = 2.4$	Fail to reject H_0
(c)	$F = \dfrac{4(10)}{(40/6)} = 6$	Reject H_0
(d)	$F = \dfrac{4(5)}{(60/6)} = 2$	Fail to reject H_0
(e)	$F = \dfrac{4(5)}{(20/6)} = 6$	Reject H_0

12.3

	A	B	C	
$\bar{x}$	22	25	27	$m = 5$ $k = 3$
s^2	6.5	5.5	8.0	

$$s_{\bar{x}}^2 = \frac{3[(22)^2 + (25)^2 + (27)^2] - (22 + 25 + 27)^2}{(3)(2)} = 6.333$$

$s_A^2 + s_B^2 + s_C^2 = 20$

H_0: $\mu_A = \mu_B = \mu_C$ H_a: Not all the means are equal $\alpha = 0.05$

12.3   Continued:

Observed value: $F = \dfrac{5(6.333)}{(20/3)} = 4.75$ df = (2,12)

Critical value: F = 3.89. Decision: Reject H_0. There is sufficient evidence to indicate that not all population means are the same.

12.4 $s_{\bar{x}}^2 = \dfrac{5[(20.75)^2 + (15.5)^2 + (16.5)^2 + (15.5)^2 + 9^2] - (20.75 + 15.5 + 16.5 + 15.5 + 9)^2}{(5)(4)}$

$= 17.7$

$s_A^2 + s_B^2 + s_C^2 + s_D^2 + s_E^2 = 133.93$

$H_0: \mu_A = \mu_B = \mu_C = \mu_D = \mu_E$ H_a: Not all the means are equal

$\alpha = 0.05$

Observed value: $F = \dfrac{4(17.7)}{(133.93/5)} = 2.64$,   df = (4,15)

Critical value: F = 3.06. Decision: Fail to reject H_0. The data do not indicate a difference in the mean daily output of the five plants.

12.5 $s_{\bar{x}}^2 = \dfrac{2[(180.3)^2 + (190.8)^2] - (180.3 + 190.8)^2}{(2)(1)} = 55.125$

$s_M^2 + s_F^2 = 166.33$

$H_0: \mu_M = \mu_F$ $H_a: \mu_M \neq \mu_F$ $\alpha = 0.01$

Observed value: $F = \dfrac{10(55.125)}{(166.33/2)} = 6.63$,   df = (1,18)

Critical value: F = 8.29. Decision: Fail to reject H_0. The data do not indicate a difference in mean heart rate maximum between male and female runners.

12.6 $\bar{x}_A = 277/6 = 46.167$ $\bar{x}_B = 330/6 = 55$ $\alpha = 0.01$

$s_A^2 = \dfrac{6(13133) - (277)^2}{(6)(5)} = 68.967$ $s_B^2 = \dfrac{6(18290) - (330)^2}{(6)(5)} = 28$

$s_{\bar{x}}^2 = \dfrac{2[(46.167)^2 + (55)^2] - (46.167 + 55)^2}{(2)(1)} = 39.011$

$H_0: \mu_A = \mu_B$ $H_a: \mu_A \neq \mu_B$

12.6   (a)   (i) $k = 2$ $n = 12$ $df = (k-1, n-k) = (1,10)$

        (ii) $F = 10.04$ (iii) $F = \dfrac{6(39.011)}{(68.967 + 28)/2} = 4.828$

        (iv) There is not sufficient evidence to reject H_0.

  (b)   (i) $df = 6 + 6 - 2 = 10$ (ii) $t = \pm 3.169$

        (iii) $t = \dfrac{55 - 46.167}{\sqrt{\dfrac{5(68.967) + 5(28)}{6 + 6 - 2}}\sqrt{\dfrac{1}{6} + \dfrac{1}{6}}} = 2.197$

        (iv) There is not sufficient evidence to reject H_0.

  (c) Note that $\sqrt{10.04} = 3.169$ and $\sqrt{4.828} \doteq 2.197$.

12.7 $s_{\bar{x}}^2 = \dfrac{5[(24)^2 + (25)^2 + (25)^2 + (30)^2 + (22)^2] - (24 + 25 + 25 + 30 + 22)^2}{(5)(4)} = 8.7$

  $s_A^2 + s_B^2 + s_C^2 + s_D^2 + s_E^2 = (5.02)^2 + (4.69)^2 + (5.66)^2 + (4.38)^2 + (4.65)^2$

                    $= 120.039$

  $H_0: \mu_A = \mu_B = \mu_C = \mu_D = \mu_E$ H_a: Not all the means are equal.

                    $\alpha = 0.05$

  (a)   (i) $k = 5$ $n = 30$ $df = (k-1, n-k) = (4,25)$

        (ii) $F = 2.76$ (iii) $F = \dfrac{6(8.7)}{(120.039)/5} = 2.17$

        (iv) There is not sufficient evidence to reject H_0.

  (b)   (i) remains the same   (ii) larger   (iii) larger

        (iv) Now

  $s_{\bar{x}}^2 = \dfrac{5[(24)^2 + (25)^2 + (25)^2 + (30)^2 + (18)^2] - (24 + 25 + 25 + 30 + 18)^2}{(5)(4)} = 18.3$

  $F = \dfrac{6(18.3)}{(120.039)/5} = 4.57.$ There is sufficient evidence to reject H_0.

12.8 $\bar{x}_A = 84/4 = 21$ $\bar{x}_B = 124/4 = 31$ $\bar{x}_C = 92/4 = 23$ $\bar{x}_D = 96/4 = 24$

  $s_A^2 = \dfrac{4(1814) - (84)^2}{(4)(3)} = 16.667$ $s_B^2 = \dfrac{4(3870) - (124)^2}{(4)(3)} = 8.667$

  $s_C^2 = \dfrac{4(2156) - (92)^2}{(4)(3)} = 13.333$ $s_D^2 = \dfrac{4(2334) - (96)^2}{(4)(3)} = 10$

12.8 Continued:

$$s_{\bar{x}} = \frac{4[(21)^2+(31)^2+(23)^2+(24)^2] - (21+31+23+24)^2}{(4)(3)} = 18.917$$

$$s_A^2 + s_B^2 + s_C^2 + s_D^2 = 48.667$$

$H_0: \mu_A = \mu_B = \mu_C = \mu_D$ $H_a:$ Not all the means are equal

$$\alpha = 0.05$$

(a) (i) $k = 4$ $n = 16$ $df = (k-1, n-k) = (3,12)$

 (ii) $F = 3.49.$ (iii) $F = \dfrac{4(18.917)}{48.667/4} = 6.22$

 (iv) There is sufficient evidence to reject H_0.

(b) (i) same   (ii) smaller   (iii) smaller

 (iv) Now

$$s_{\bar{x}}^2 = \frac{4[(21)^2+(27)^2+(23)^2+(24)^2] - (21 + 27 + 23 + 24)^2}{(4)(3)} = 6.25$$

$$F = \frac{4(6.25)}{48.667/4} = 2.05.$$

There is not sufficient evidence to reject H_0.

12.9 $\sum x_A = 81$ $\bar{x}_A = 27$ $\sum(x_A - \bar{x}_A)^2 = 18$ $n_A = 3$ $\sum x_B = 175$ $\bar{x}_B = 35$

$\sum(x_B - \bar{x}_B)^2 = 58$ $n_B = 5$

$SSW = 18 + 58 = 76$ $MSW = SSW/(n-k) = 76/(8-2) = 12.667$

$\bar{\bar{x}} = (81 + 175)/8 = 32$ $SSB = 3(27 - 32)^2 + 5(35 - 32)^2 = 120$

$MSB = SSB/(k-1) = 120/(2 - 1) = 120$

Source	SS	df	MS	F-statistic
Between samples	120	1	120	9.47
Within samples	76	6	12.667	
Total	196	7		

$H_0: \mu_A = \mu_B$ $H_a: \mu_A \neq \mu_B$ $\alpha = 0.05$

Observed value: $F = 120/12.667 = 9.47$ $df = (1,6)$

Critical value: $F = 5.99.$ Decision: Reject H_0.

12.10 $\sum x_A = 128$ $\bar{x}_A = 32$ $\sum (x_A - \bar{x}_A)^2 = 110$ $n_A = 4$ $\sum x_B = 100$ $\bar{x}_B = 25$

$\sum (x_B - \bar{x}_B)^2 = 86$ $n_B = 4$

SSW = 110 + 86 = 196.   MSW = SSW/(n-k) = 196/(8-2) = 32.667.

$\bar{\bar{x}}$ = (128 + 100)/8 = 28.5   SSB = $4(32-28.5)^2 + 4(25-28.5)^2 = 98$

MSB = SSB/(k-1) = 98/(2-1) = 98

Source	SS	df	MS	F-statistic
Between samples	98	1	98	3
Within samples	196	6	32.667	
Total	294	7		

$H_0: \mu_A = \mu_B$ $H_a: \mu_A \neq \mu_B$ $\alpha = 0.05$

Observed value: F = 98/32.667 = 3   df = (1,6)

Critical value: F = 5.99. Decision: Fail to reject H_0.

12.11 $\sum x_A = 36$ $\bar{x}_A = 12$ $\sum (x_A - \bar{x}_A)^2 = 24$ $n_A = 3$ $\sum x_B = 18$ $\bar{x}_B = 6$

$\sum (x_B - \bar{x}_B)^2 = 18$ $n_B = 3$ $\sum x_C = 28$ $\bar{x}_C = 7$ $\sum (x_C - \bar{x}_C)^2 = 20$ $n_C = 4$

SSW = 24 + 18 + 20 = 62   MSW = SSW/(n-k) = 62/(10-3) = 8.86

$\bar{\bar{x}}$ = (36 + 18 + 28)/10 = 8.2

SSB = $3(12 - 8.2)^2 + 3(6 - 8.2)^2 + 4(7 - 8.2)^2 = 63.6$

MSB = SSB/(k-1) = 63.6/2 = 31.8

Source	SS	df	MS	F-statistic
Between samples	63.6	2	31.8	3.59
Within samples	62	7	8.86	
Total	125.6	9		

$H_0: \mu_A = \mu_B = \mu_C$ H_a: Not all the means are equal

$\alpha = 0.05$

Observed value: F = 31.8/8.86 = 3.59. Critical value: 4.74

Decision: Fail to reject H_0.   df = (2,7)

12.12 $\sum x_A = 18$ $\bar{x}_A = 6$ $\sum(x_A - \bar{x}_A)^2 = 56$ $n_A = 3$ $\sum x_B = 12$ $\bar{x}_B = 6$

$\sum(x_B - \bar{x}_B)^2 = 32$ $n_B = 2$ $\sum x_C = 32$ $\bar{x}_C = 8$ $\sum(x_C - \bar{x}_C)^2 = 48$ $n_C = 4$

$\sum x_D = 80$ $\bar{x}_D = 16$ $\sum(x_D - \bar{x}_D)^2 = 54$ $n_D = 5$

SSW $= 56 + 32 + 48 + 54 = 190$ MSW $=$ SSW/$(n-k) = 190/(14-4) = 19$

$\bar{\bar{x}} = (18 + 12 + 32 + 80)/14 = 10.143$

SSB $= 3(6-10.143)^2 + 2(6-10.143)^2 + 4(8-10.143)^2 + 5(16-10.143)^2$

$\qquad = 275.714$

MSB $=$ SSB/$(k-1) = 275.714/3 = 91.905$.

Source	SS	df	MS	F-statistic
Between samples	275.714	3	91.905	4.84
Within samples	190	10	19	
Total	465.71	13		

$H_0: \mu_A = \mu_B = \mu_C = \mu_D$ H_a: Not all the means are equal.

$\qquad\qquad\qquad\qquad\qquad\qquad\qquad\alpha = 0.05$

Observed value: $F = 91.905/19 = 4.84$ df $= (3,10)$

Critical value: $F = 3.71$.   Decision: Reject H_0.

12.13 (a)

Source	SS	df	MS	F-statistic
Between samples	250	5	50	8.33
Within samples	150	25	6	
Total	400	30		

(b) $H_0: \mu_A = \mu_B = \mu_C = \mu_D = \mu_E = \mu_F$ H_a: Not all the means are equal.

$\qquad\qquad\qquad\qquad\qquad\alpha = 0.05$

Observed value: $F = 50/6 = 8.33$, df $= (5,25)$

Critical value: $F = 2.60$. Decision: Reject H_0.

12.14

(a)

Source	SS	df	MS	F-statistic
Between samples	180	3	60	6
Within samples	120	12	10	
Total	300	15		

(b) H_0: $\mu_A = \mu_B = \mu_C = \mu_D$. H_a: Not all the means are equal.

$$\alpha = 0.01$$

Observed value: $F = 60/10 = 6$, df $= (3,12)$

Critical value: $F = 5.95$. Decision: Reject H_0.

12.15

(a)

Source	SS	df	MS	F-statistic
Between samples	128	4	32	2
Within samples	160	10	16	
Total	288	14		

(b) H_0: $\mu_A = \mu_B = \mu_C = \mu_D = \mu_E$. H_a: Not all the means are equal.

$$\alpha = 0.05$$

Observed value: $F = 32/16 = 2$, df $= (4,10)$.

Critical value: $F = 3.48$. Decision: Fail to reject H_0.

12.16

(a)

Source	SS	df	MS	F-statistic
Between samples	100	2	50	12.5
Within samples	160	40	4	
Total	260	42		

(b) H_0: $\mu_A = \mu_B = \mu_C$. H_a: Not all the means are equal. $\alpha=0.01$

Observed value: $F = 50/4 = 12.5$, df $= (2,40)$.

Critical value: $F = 5.18$. Decision: Reject H_0.

12.17 H_0: $\mu_A = \mu_B = \mu_C$. H_a: Not all the means are equal. $\alpha = 0.05$

SSW $= 656 + 746 + 948 = 2350$. MSW $= 2350/(19-3) = 146.875$.

SSB$=5(66-73.789)^2+6(68-73.789)^2+8(83-73.789)^2=1183.158$

MSB $= 1183.158/(3 - 1) = 591.579$.

Observed value: $F = 591.579/146.875 = 4.03$, df $= (2,16)$.

12.17 Continued:

Critical value: $F = 3.63$. Decision: Reject H_0. There is sufficient evidence to indicate that not all population means are the same.

12.18 $H_0: \mu_A = \mu_C$ $H_a: \mu_A \neq \mu_C$ $\alpha = 0.05$

(a) SSW $= 656 + 948 = 1604$ MSW $= 1604/11 = 145.818$

SSB $= 5(66 - 76.462)^2 + 8(83 - 76.462)^2 = 889.231$

MSB $= 889.231/(2 - 1) = 889.231$

Observed value: $F = 889.231/145.818 = 6.1$,   df $= (1,11)$

Critical value: $F = 4.84$. Decision: Reject H_0. There is sufficient evidence to indicate a difference in population means between A and C.

(b) Observed value:

$$t = -\frac{83 - 66}{\sqrt{\dfrac{4(12.81)^2 + 7(11.64)^2}{5 + 8 - 2}}\sqrt{\dfrac{1}{5} + \dfrac{1}{8}}} = 2.47, \quad df = 11$$

Critical values: $t = \pm 2.201$. Decision: Reject H_0.

Note: $t^2 = (2.47)^2 = F = 6.1$.

12.19 $H_0: \mu_A = \mu_B = \mu_C = \mu_D$ H_a: Not all the means are equal.
$$\alpha = 0.05$$

SSW $= 3(0.768)^2 + 4(0.554)^2 + 5(0.652)^2 + 8(0.97)^2 = 12.65$

MSW $= 12.65/(24 - 4) = 0.633$

SSB $= 4(6.775 - 6.254)^2 + 5(7.22 - 6.254)^2 + 6(6.017 - 6.254)^2$
$$+ 9(5.644 - 6.254)^2 = 9.437$$

MSB $= 9.437/(4 - 1) = 3.146$

Observed value: $F = 3.146/0.633 = 4.97$,   df $= (3,20)$

Critical value: $F = 3.10$. Decision: Reject H_0. The data indicate not all population means are the same in the 4 regions.

12.20 $H_0: \mu_E = \mu_G = \mu_N$ H_a: Not all the means are equal. $\alpha = 0.01$
SSW $= 19(12.1)^2 + 7(10.9)^2 + 71(10.5)^2 = 11441.21$

MSW $= 11441.21/(100 - 3) = 117.951$

SSB $= 20(56-50.64)^2 + 8(52-50.64)^2 + 72(49-50.64)^2 = 783.04$

MSB $= 783.04/(3 - 1) = 391.52$

12.20 Continued:

Observed value: $F = 391.52/117.951 = 3.32$, df $= (2,97)$

Critical value: $F = 4.98$. Decision: Fail to reject H_0. The data do not support the claim.

12.21 H_0: $\mu_{CR} = \mu_M = \mu_{CO}$ H_a: Not all the means are equal.

$$\alpha = 0.01$$

$SSW = 27(4.5)^2 + 33(4.6)^2 + 33(5.2)^2 = 2137.35$

$MSW = 2137.35/(96 - 3) = 22.982$

$SSB = 28(26.5-27.81)^2 + 34(25.5-27.81)^2 + 34(31.2-27.81)^2 = 620.21$

$MSB = 620.21/(3 - 1) = 310.105$

Observed value: $F = 310.105/22.982 = 13.49$, df $= (2,93)$

Critical value: $F = 4.98$. Decision: Reject H_0. The data indicate not all mean percent calories from fats are the same.

12.22 (a)

Source	SS	df	MS	F-statistic
Between samples	24	2	12	2.4
Within samples	30	6	5	
Total	54	8		

H_0: $\mu_A = \mu_B = \mu_C$ H_a: Not all the means are equal. $\alpha = 0.05$

Observed value: $F = 12/5 = 2.4$, df $= (2,6)$

Critical value: $F = 5.14$. Decision: Fail to reject H_0.

(b) (i) Note that SSB will change, but SSW will not. So SSB will be larger, hence F will be increased. Also, TSS will increase. The remaining parts of the table will remain the same.

(ii) $SSB = 3(3-7)^2 + 3(5-7)^2 + 3(13-7)^2 = 168$

$MSB = 168/2 = 84$ $F = 84/5 = 16.8$

Source	SS	df	MS	F-statistic
Between samples	168	2	84	16.8
Within samples	30	6	5	
Total	198	8		

12.22

(c) (i) SSB will be smaller and SSW unchanged. So F will be smaller. Also, TSS will be smaller. The remaining parts of the table will remain the same.

(ii) $SSB = 3(6-6)^2 + 3(5-6)^2 + 3(7-6)^2 = 6$

$MSB = 6/2 = 3$ $F = 3/5 = 0.6$

Source	SS	df	MS	F-statistic
Between samples	6	2	3	0.6
Within samples	30	6	5	
Total	36	8		

12.23 $T_A = 81$ $n_A = 3$ $T_B = 175$ $n_B = 5$

(a)

$$SSB = \frac{81^2}{3} + \frac{175^2}{5} - \frac{(81 + 175)^2}{8} = 120$$

$$SSW = 30^2 + 27^2 + 24^2 + 35^2 + 37^2 + 33^2 + 30^2 + 40^2 - \left(\frac{81^2}{3} + \frac{175^2}{5}\right) = 76$$

(b) $T_A = 128$ $n_A = 4$ $T_B = 100$ $n_B = 4$

$$SSB = \frac{128^2}{4} + \frac{100^2}{4} - \frac{(128 + 100)^2}{8} = 98$$

$$SSW = 29^2 + 38^2 + 25^2 + 36^2 + 26^2 + 31^2 + 25^2 + 18^2 - \left(\frac{128^2}{4} + \frac{100^2}{4}\right) = 196$$

(c) $T_A = 36$ $n_A = 3$ $T_B = 18$ $n_B = 3$ $T_C = 28$ $n_C = 4$

$$SSB = \frac{36^2}{3} + \frac{18^2}{3} + \frac{28^2}{4} - \frac{(36 + 18 + 28)^2}{10} = 63.6$$

$$SSW = 10^2 + 16^2 + 10^2 + 9^2 + 3^2 + 6^2 + 8^2 + 10^2 + 4^2 + 6^2 - \left(\frac{36^2}{3} + \frac{18^2}{3} + \frac{28^2}{4}\right) = 62$$

(d) $T_A = 18$ $n_A = 3$ $T_B = 12$ $n_B = 2$ $T_C = 32$ $n_C = 4$ $T_D = 80$ $n_D = 5$

$$SSB = \frac{18^2}{3} + \frac{12^2}{2} + \frac{32^2}{4} + \frac{80^2}{5} - \frac{(18 + 12 + 32 + 80)^2}{14} = 275.71$$

$$SSW = 12^2 + 2^2 + 4^2 + 10^2 + 2^2 + 6^2 + 6^2 + 14^2 + 6^2 + 22^2 + 16^2 + 16^2 + 13^2 + 13^2 - \left(\frac{18^2}{3} + \frac{12^2}{2} + \frac{32^2}{4} + \frac{80^2}{5}\right) = 190$$

12.24 $H_0: \mu_A = \mu_B = \mu_C = \mu_D$ H_a: Not all the means are equal

df $= (4 - 1, 24 - 4) = (3, 20)$ $\alpha = 0.01$

  Critical value: $F = 4.94$.

	Observed value	Decision
(a)	$F = \dfrac{6(4)}{24/4} = 4$	Fail to reject H_0
(b)	$F = \dfrac{6(2.5)}{24/4} = 2.5$	Fail to reject H_0
(c)	$F = \dfrac{6(6)}{24/4} = 6$	Reject H_0
(d)	$F = \dfrac{6(4)}{48/4} = 2$	Fail to reject H_0
(e)	$F = \dfrac{6(4)}{12/4} = 8$	Reject H_0

12.25 $SSW = \sum(x_A - \bar{x}_A)^2 + \sum(x_B - \bar{x}_B)^2 + \sum(x_C - \bar{x}_C)^2 = 50 + 50 + 100 = 200$

$MSW = 200/(10 - 3) = 28.571$

$SSB = n_A(\bar{x}_A - \bar{\bar{x}})^2 + n_B(\bar{x}_B - \bar{\bar{x}})^2 + n_C(\bar{x}_C - \bar{\bar{x}})^2$

     $= 2(110.25) + 3(0.25) + 5(20.25) = 322.5$

$MSB = 322.5/(3 - 1) = 161.25$

$F = 161.25/28.571 = 5.64$

Source	SS	df	MS	F-statistic
Between samples	322.5	2	161.25	5.64
Within samples	200	7	28.571	
Total	522.5	9		

$H_0: \mu_A = \mu_B = \mu_C$ H_a: Not all the means are equal $\alpha = 0.05$

Observed value: $F = 5.64$,   df $= (2, 7)$

Critical value: $F = 4.74$.   Decision: Reject H_0.

12.26 $\text{SSW} = \sum (x_A - \bar{x}_A)^2 + \sum (x_B - \bar{x}_B)^2 + \sum (x_C - \bar{x}_C)^2 + \sum (x_D - \bar{x}_D)^2$

$= 54 + 50 + 72 + 32 = 208$

$\text{MSW} = 208/(12 - 4) = 26$

$\text{SSB} = n_A(\bar{x}_A - \bar{\bar{x}})^2 + n_B(\bar{x}_B - \bar{\bar{x}})^2 + n_C(\bar{x}_C - \bar{\bar{x}})^2 + n_D(\bar{x}_D - \bar{\bar{x}})^2$

$= 3(33.063) + (3)(1.563) + 4(0.563) + 2(68.063) = 242.25$

$\text{MSB} = 242.25/(4 - 1) = 80.75$

$F = 80.75/26 = 3.11$

Source	SS	df	MS	F-statistic
Between samples	242.25	3	80.75	3.11
Within samples	208	8	26	
Total	450.25	11		

$H_0: \mu_A = \mu_B = \mu_C = \mu_D$ H_a: Not all the means are equal

$\alpha = 0.05$

Observed value: $F = 3.11$, $df = (3,8)$

Critical value: $F = 4.07$. Decision: Fail to reject H_0.

12.27
(a)

Source	SS	df	MS	F-statistic
Between samples	132	4	33	3.3
Within samples	400	40	10	
Total	532	44		

(b) $H_0: \mu_A = \mu_B = \mu_C = \mu_D = \mu_E$ H_a: Not all the means are equal

$\alpha = 0.05$

Observed value: $F = 33/10 = 3.3$, $df = (4,40)$

Critical value: $F = 2.61$. Decision: Reject H_0.

12.28
(a)

Source	SS	df	MS	F-statistic
Between samples	54	3	18	1.5
Within samples	240	20	12	
Total	294	23		

12.28 (b) H_0: $\mu_A = \mu_B = \mu_C = \mu_D$ H_a: Not all the means are equal.

$\alpha = 0.01$

Observed value: $F = 18/12 = 1.5$,   df $= (3,20)$

Critical value: $F = 4.94$.   Decision: Fail to reject H_0.

12.29 $\sum x_A = 240$ $\bar{x}_A = 60$ $\sum (x_A - \bar{x}_A)^2 = 288$ $n_A = 4$

$\sum x_B = 162$ $\bar{x}_B = 54$ $\sum (x_B - \bar{x}_B)^2 = 86$ $n_B = 3$

$\sum x_C = 160$ $\bar{x}_C = 40$ $\sum (x_C - \bar{x}_C)^2 = 200$ $n_C = 4$

$\bar{\bar{x}} = (240 + 162 + 160)/11 = 51.091$

SSW $= 288 + 86 + 200 = 574$

MSW $= 574/(11 - 3) = 71.75$

SSB $= 4(60-51.091)^2 + 3(54-51.091)^2 + 4(40-51.091)^2 = 834.909$

MSB $= 834.909/(3 - 1) = 417.455$

H_0: $\mu_A = \mu_B = \mu_C$ H_a: Not all the means are equal.

$\alpha = 0.05$

Observed value: $F = 417.455/71.75 = 5.82$,   df $= (2,8)$

Critical value: $F = 4.46$.   Decision: Reject H_0.

12.30 $\sum x_A = 120$ $\bar{x}_A = 40$ $\sum (x_A - \bar{x}_A)^2 = 350$ $n_A = 3$

$\sum x_B = 120$ $\bar{x}_B = 24$ $\sum (x_B - \bar{x}_B)^2 = 470$ $n_B = 5$

$\bar{\bar{x}} = (120 + 120)/8 = 30$.   SSW $= 350 + 470 = 820$.

MSW $= 820/(8 - 2) = 136.667$.

SSB $= 3(40 - 30)^2 + 5(24 - 30)^2 = 480$.

MSB $= 480/(2 - 1) = 480$.

H_0: $\mu_A = \mu_B$ H_a: $\mu_A \neq \mu_B$ $\alpha = 0.05$

Observed value: $F = 480/136.667 = 3.51$,   df $= (1,6)$

Critical value: $F = 5.99$.   Decision: Fail to reject H_0.

12.31 $\sum x_A = 14.4$ $\bar{x}_A = 2.4$ $\sum (x_A - \bar{x}_A)^2 = 0.44$ $n_A = 6$

$\sum x_B = 16.8$ $\bar{x}_B = 2.8$ $\sum (x_B - \bar{x}_B)^2 = 0.44$ $n_B = 6$

$\sum x_C = 15$ $\bar{x}_C = 3$ $\sum (x_C - \bar{x}_C)^2 = 0.34$ $n_C = 5$

$\bar{\bar{x}} = (14.4 + 16.8 + 15)/17 = 2.718$

$SSW = 0.44 + 0.44 + 0.34 = 1.22$

$MSW = 1.22/(17 - 3) = 0.087$

$SSB = 6(2.4 - 2.718)^2 + 6(2.8 - 2.718)^2 + 5(3 - 2.718)^2 = 1.045$

$MSB = 1.045/(3 - 1) = 0.523$

$H_0: \mu_A = \mu_B = \mu_C$ H_a: Not all the means are equal. $\alpha = 0.05$

Observed value: $F = 0.523/0.087 = 6.01$,   df = (2,14)

Critical value: F = 3.74. Decision: Reject H_0. The data indicate that not all population means are the same for the 3 schools.

12.32 $\sum x_A = 70$ $\bar{x}_A = 14$ $\sum (x_A - \bar{x}_A)^2 = 30$ $n_A = 5$

$\sum x_B = 68$ $\bar{x}_B = 17$ $\sum (x_B - \bar{x}_B)^2 = 20$ $n_B = 4$

$\sum x_C = 60$ $\bar{x}_C = 20$ $\sum (x_C - \bar{x}_C)^2 = 26$ $n_C = 3$

$\sum x_D = 60$ $\bar{x}_D = 15$ $\sum (x_D - \bar{x}_D)^2 = 26$ $n_D = 4$

$\bar{\bar{x}} = (70 + 68 + 60 + 60)/16 = 16.125$

$SSW = 30 + 20 + 26 + 26 = 102$ $MSW = 102/(16 - 4) = 8.5$

$SSB = 5(14-16.125)^2 + 4(17-16.125)^2 + 3(20-16.125)^2 + 4(15-16.125)^2$

        $= 75.75$

$MSB = 75.75/(4 - 1) = 25.25$

$H_0: \mu_A = \mu_B = \mu_C = \mu_D$ H_a: Not all the means are equal

                                    $\alpha = 0.05$

Observed value: $F = 25.25/8.5 = 2.97$, df = (3,12)

Critical value: F = 3.49. Decision: Fail to reject H_0. The data do not indicate a difference in population mean time between the 4 plants.

12.33 $s_A^2=80$ $s_B^2=50$ $s_C^2=70$ $\bar{x}_A=36$ $\bar{x}_B=38$ $\bar{x}_C=50$ $s_{\bar{x}}^2 = 57.333$

$H_0\colon \mu_A = \mu_B = \mu_C$ $H_a\colon$ Not all the means are equal

$$\alpha = 0.05$$

Observed value: $F = \dfrac{5(57.333)}{(80 + 50 + 70)/3} = 4.3,$ df = (2,12)

Critical value: F = 3.89. Decision: Reject H_0. There
is sufficient evidence to indicate not all population
mean percentage of sales are the same.

12.34 $s_B^2 = 50$ $s_C^2 = 70$ $\bar{x}_B = 38$ $\bar{x}_C = 50$ $s_{\bar{x}}^2 = 72$

$H_0\colon \mu_B^2 = \mu_C^2$ $H_a\colon \mu_B^2 \neq \mu_C^2$ $\alpha = 0.05$

Observed value: $F = \dfrac{5(72)}{(50 + 70)/2} = 6,$ df = (1,8)

Critical value: F = 5.32. Decision: Reject H_0. There is
sufficient evidence to indicate a difference in population
mean percentage of sales between stores B and C.

12.35 Let A, B, and C represent elite, good, and nonrunners
respectively.

$H_0\colon \mu_A = \mu_B = \mu_C$ $H_a\colon$ Not all the means are equal.

$$\alpha = 0.05$$

SSW = $19(24.5)^2 + 7(29.5)^2 + 71(35.6)^2 = 107479.06$

MSW = $107479.06/(100 - 3) = 1108.032$

$\bar{\bar{x}} = \dfrac{20(108) + 8(121) + 72(124)}{100} = 120.56$

SSB = $20(108-120.56)^2 + 8(121-120.56)^2 + 72(124-120.56)^2$

   = 4008.64

MSB = $4008.64/(3 - 1) = 2004.32$

Observed value: F = 2004.32/1108.032 = 1.81, df = (2,97)

Critical value: F = 3.15. Decision: Fail to reject H_0.
The data do not indicate a difference in population
mean LDL cholesterol between the 3 groups of runners.

12.36 Let A, B, and C represent Crevalcore, Montegiorgio and Crete respectively.

H_0: $\mu_A = \mu_B = \mu_C$ H_a: Not all the means are equal.

$\alpha = 0.05$

SSW = $27(1.7)^2 + 33(1.7)^2 + 29(2.2)^2 = 313.76$

MSW = $313.76/(92-3) = 3.525$

$\bar{\bar{x}} = \dfrac{28(13) + 34(11.7) + 30(11.2)}{92} = 11.933$

SSB = $28(13-11.933)^2 + 34(11.7-11.933)^2 + 30(11.2-11.933)^2$

    = 49.842

MSB = $49.842/(3-1) = 24.921$

Observed value: $F = 24.921/3.525 = 7.07$,   df = (2,89)

Critical value: $F = 3.15$. Decision: Reject H_0. The data indicate that not all population mean percent calories from protein are the same for the 3 groups.

12.37 (i)

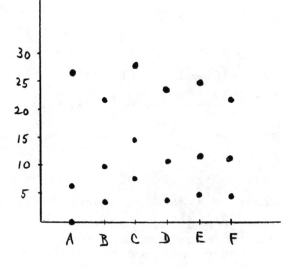

12.37 (ii) $s_A^2 = 103$ $\bar{x}_A = 9$ $s_B^2 = 84$ $\bar{x}_B = 12$ $s_C^2 = 103$ $\bar{x}_C = 17$

$s_D^2 = 103$ $\bar{x}_D = 13$ $s_E^2 = 103$ $\bar{x}_E = 14$ $s_F^2 = 73$ $\bar{x}_F = 13$

$s_{\bar{x}}^2 = 6.8$

$H_0:$ $\mu_A = \mu_B = \mu_C = \mu_D = \mu_E = \mu_F$ $H_a:$ Not all the means are equal.

$$\alpha = 0.05$$

Observed value: $F = \dfrac{3(6.8)}{(103+84+103+103+103+73)/6} = 0.215,$

$$df = (5,12)$$

Critical value: $F = 3.11.$ Decision: Fail to reject $H_0.$

12.38 (i)

(ii) $s_A^2 = 7.2$ $s_B^2 = 6.8$ $s_C^2 = 7.6$ $\bar{x}_A = 3$ $\bar{x}_B = 9$ $\bar{x}_C = 21$ $s_{\bar{x}}^2 = 84$

$H_0:$ $\mu_A = \mu_B = \mu_C$ $H_a:$ Not all the means are equal.

$$\alpha = 0.05$$

Observed value: $F = \dfrac{6(84)}{(7.2 + 6.8 + 7.6)/3} = 70,$ $df = (2,15)$

Critical value: $F = 3.68.$ Decision: Reject $H_0.$

12.39 (a) The ANOVA table is identical with that obtained in exercise 12.38.

(b) By adding 2 to each data value, the variance of the means and the variance within each sample remains the same.

13.1 H_0: $P_1=P_2=P_3=P_4=1/4$. H_a: H_0 is not true. $\alpha = 0.05$.

Observed value:
$$\chi^2 = \sum \frac{(O-E)^2}{E} = \frac{(68-75)^2}{75} + \frac{(65-75)^2}{75} + \frac{(77-75)^2}{75} + \frac{(90-75)^2}{75} = 5.04$$

$$df = 4 - 1 = 3$$

Critical value: $\chi^2 = 7.815$. Decision: Fail to reject H_0.

13.2 H_0: $P_1=P_2=P_3=1/5$, $P_4=2/5$. H_a: H_0 is not true. $\alpha = 0.01$

Observed value:
$$\chi^2 = \sum \frac{(O-E)^2}{E} = \frac{(68-60)^2}{60} + \frac{(65-60)^2}{60} + \frac{(77-60)^2}{60} + \frac{(90-120)^2}{120} = 13.80$$

$$df = 4 - 1 = 3$$

Critical value: $\chi^2 = 11.345$. Decision: Reject H_0.

13.3 H_0:$P_1=P_2=1/10$, $P_3=P_4=1/5$, $P_5=2/5$ H_a:H_0 is not true.

$$\alpha = 0.10$$

Observed value:
$$\chi^2 = \sum \frac{(O-E)^2}{E} = \frac{(12-12)^2}{12} + \frac{(20-12)^2}{12} + \frac{(20-24)^2}{24} + \frac{(30-24)^2}{24} + \frac{(38-48)^2}{48}$$

$$= 9.58 \qquad df = 5 - 1 = 4$$

Critical value: $\chi^2 = 7.779$. Decision: Reject H_0.

13.4 H_0: $P_1=P_2=P_3=P_4=P_5=P_6= 1/6$ H_a: H_0 is not true.

$$\alpha = 0.05$$

Observed value:
$$\chi^2 = \sum \frac{(O-E)^2}{E} = \frac{(7-10)^2}{10} + \frac{(6-10)^2}{10} + \frac{(7-10)^2}{10} + \frac{(18-10)^2}{10} + \frac{(15-10)^2}{10}$$

$$+ \frac{(7-10)^2}{10} = 13.2 \qquad df = 6 - 1 = 5$$

Critical value: $\chi^2 = 11.071$. Decision: Reject H_0.

13.5 Let A,B,C, and D represent white females, black females, white males, and black males respectively.

H_0: $P_A=0.3$, $P_B=0.05$, $P_C=0.5$, $P_D =0.15$.

H_a: H_0 is not true. $\alpha = 0.05$.

13.5 Continued:

Observed value:

$$\chi^2 = \sum \frac{(O-E)^2}{E} = \frac{(40-45)^2}{45} + \frac{(15-7.5)^2}{7.5} + \frac{(80-75)^2}{75} + \frac{(15-22.5)^2}{22.5}$$

$$= 10.89 \qquad df = 4 - 1 = 3$$

Critical value: $\chi^2 = 7.815$. Decision: Reject H_0. There is sufficient evidence to reject the official's claim.

13.6 Let D, R, and I represent Democrats, Republicans, and Independents respectively.

$$H_0: P_D = 0.45, \quad P_R = 0.17, \quad P_I = 0.38. \qquad H_a: H_0 \text{ is not true.}$$

$$\alpha = 0.05$$

Observed value:

$$\chi^2 = \sum \frac{(O-E)^2}{E} = \frac{(18-23.85)^2}{23.85} + \frac{(11-9.01)^2}{9.01} + \frac{(24-20.14)^2}{20.14} = 2.61$$

$$df = 3 - 1 = 2$$

Critical value: $\chi^2 = 5.991$. Decision: Fail to reject H_0. There is insufficient evidence to conclude that party affiliation for women at the university differs from nationwide party affiliation.

13.7 Let A, B, C, and D represent less than \$20,000, between \$20,000 and \$25,000, between \$25,000 and \$30,000, and more than \$30,000 respectively.

$$H_0: P_A = 1/10, \quad P_B = P_C = P_D = 3/10 \qquad H_a: H_0 \text{ is not true. } \alpha = 0.10$$

Observed value:

$$\chi^2 = \sum \frac{(O-E)^2}{E} = \frac{(19-16.6)^2}{16.6} + \frac{(56-49.8)^2}{49.8} + \frac{(51-49.8)^2}{49.8} + \frac{(40-49.8)^2}{49.8}$$

$$= 3.08 \qquad df = 4 - 1 = 3$$

Critical value: $\chi^2 = 6.251$. Decision: Fail to reject H_0. There is insufficient evidence to refute the owner's claim.

13.8　　Let A, B, C, and D represent less than 10 points,
　　　　　　　between 10 and 19 points inclusive, between 20
　　　and 29 points inclusive, and more than 29 points respec-
　　　tively.

H_0: p_A=0.50, p_B=0.25, p_C=0.20, p_D=0.05.

H_a: H_0 is not true.　　　α = 0.05.

Observed value:

$$\chi^2 = \sum \frac{(O-E)^2}{E} = \frac{(70-56)^2}{56} + \frac{(20-28)^2}{28} + \frac{(13-22.4)^2}{22.4} + \frac{(9-5.6)^2}{5.6}$$

$$= 11.79 \qquad\qquad df = 4 - 1 = 3$$

Critical value: $\chi^2 = 7.815$. Decision: Reject H_0. There
is sufficient evidence to reject the claim.

13.9　　H_0: $p = 1/10$ for each category. H_a:H_0 is not true. α =0.05

Observed value:

$$\chi^2 = \sum \frac{(O-E)^2}{E} = \frac{(6-10)^2}{10} + \frac{(6-10)^2}{10} + \frac{(13-10)^2}{10} + \frac{(9-10)^2}{10} + \frac{(13-10)^2}{10}$$

$$+ \frac{(11-10)^2}{10} + \frac{(8-10)^2}{10} + \frac{(12-10)^2}{10} + \frac{(10-10)^2}{10} + \frac{(12-10)^2}{10} = 6.4$$

$$df = 10 - 1 = 9$$

Critical value: $\chi^2 = 16.919$. Decision: Fail to reject H_0.
There is insufficient evidence to reject the claim.

13.10　　Let A,B,C,D,E,F,G, and H represent the categories from
　　　less than or equal to -1.16 through more than 1.16
　　　respectively.　Using table B-3, we obtain H_0.　[For
　　　example, $P(z < -1.16) = 0.1230$.]

H_0: p_A=0.1230, p_B=0.1252, p_C=0.1263, p_D=0.1255, p_E=0.1255,

　　p_F=0.1263, p_G=0.1252, p_H=0.1230. H_a: H_0 is not true.

　　α = 0.10.

Observed value:

$$\chi^2 = \sum \frac{(O-E)^2}{E} = \frac{(7-7.38)^2}{7.38} + \frac{(7-7.52)^2}{7.51} + \frac{(6-7.57)^2}{7.58} + \frac{(7-7.53)^2}{7.53}$$

$$+ \frac{(13-7.53)^2}{7.53} + \frac{(5-7.57)^2}{7.58} + \frac{(9-7.52)^2}{7.51} + \frac{(6-7.38)^2}{7.38} = 5.83$$

$$df = 8 - 1 = 7$$

Critical value: $\chi^2 = 12.017$. Decision: Fail to reject H_0.

13.10 Continued:

There is insufficient evidence to conclude the data were sampled from a nonnormal distribution.

13.11 H_0: Characteristics of ratings and age are independent.

H_a: Characteristics of ratings and age are related.

$\alpha = 0.05$

Observed value: $\chi^2 = \sum \dfrac{(O-E)^2}{E} = \dfrac{(6-8.32)^2}{8.32} + \dfrac{(12-9.36)^2}{9.36}$

$+ \dfrac{(8-8.32)^2}{8.32} + \dfrac{(10-7.68)^2}{7.68} + \dfrac{(6-8.64)^2}{8.64} + \dfrac{(8-7.68)^2}{7.68} = 2.92$

$df = (2 - 1)(3 - 1) = 2$

Critical value: $\chi^2 = 5.991$. Decision: Fail to reject H_0. There is insufficient evidence to suggest that ratings and age are related.

13.12 H_0: Characteristics of sex and political affiliation are independent.

H_a: Characteristics of sex and political affiliation are related.

$\alpha = 0.10$

Observed value: $\chi^2 = \sum \dfrac{(O-E)^2}{E} = \dfrac{(20-14.73)^2}{14.73} + \dfrac{(10-9.33)^2}{9.33}$

$+ \dfrac{(25-30.94)^2}{30.94} + \dfrac{(10-15.27)^2}{15.27} + \dfrac{(9-9.67)^2}{9.67} + \dfrac{(38-32.06)^2}{32.06} = 6.04$

$df = (2 - 1)(3 - 1) = 2$

Critical value: 4.605. Decision: Reject H_0. The data indicate that the characteristics of sex and political affiliation are related.

13.13 H_0: The characteristics of gender and CHD are independent.

H_a: The characteristics of gender and CHD are related.

$\alpha = 0.05$

Observed value: $\chi^2 = \sum \dfrac{(O-E)^2}{E} = \dfrac{(5-5.89)^2}{5.89} + \dfrac{(6-5.11)^2}{5.11}$

$+ \dfrac{(10-9.11)^2}{9.11} + \dfrac{(7-7.89)^2}{7.89} = 0.48 \qquad df = (2 - 1)(2 - 1) = 1$

Critical value: $\chi^2 = 3.841$. Decision: Fail to reject H_0. The data do not indicate that gender and CHD are related.

13.14 H_0: The characteristics of union affiliation and political preference are independent. H_a: The characteristics of union affiliation and political preference are related.
$\alpha = 0.05$

Observed value: $\chi^2 = \sum \dfrac{(O-E)^2}{E} = \dfrac{(80-68.25)^2}{68.25} + \dfrac{(15-22.75)^2}{22.75}$

$+ \dfrac{(35-39)^2}{39} + \dfrac{(25-36.75)^2}{36.75} + \dfrac{(20-12.25)^2}{12.25} + \dfrac{(25-21)^2}{21} = 14.5$

$df = (2-1)(3-1) = 2$

Critical value: $\chi^2 = 5.991$. Decision: Reject H_0. The data indicate that the characteristics of union affiliation and political preference are related.

13.15 H_0: The characteristics of sex and salaries are independent. H_a: The characteristics of sex and salaries are related. $\alpha = 0.10$

Observed value:

$\chi^2 = \sum \dfrac{(O-E)^2}{E} = \dfrac{(12-8.58)^2}{8.58} + \dfrac{(30-25.3)^2}{25.3} + \dfrac{(20-23.04)^2}{23.04}$

$+ \dfrac{(13-18.07)^2}{18.07} + \dfrac{(7-10.42)^2}{10.42} + \dfrac{(26-30.7)^2}{30.7} + \dfrac{(31-27.96)^2}{27.96}$

$+ \dfrac{(27-21.93)^2}{21.93} = 7.4 \qquad df = (2-1)(4-1) = 3$

Critical value: $\chi^2 = 6.251$. Decision: Reject H_0. The data indicate that the characteristics of sex and salaries are related.

13.16 H_0: The characteristics of belief about public funding of abortions and political affiliation are independent.

H_a: The characteristics of belief about public funding of abortions and political affiliation are related.

$\alpha = 0.05$

Observed value: $\chi^2 = \sum \dfrac{(O-E)^2}{E} = \dfrac{(9-9.96)^2}{9.96} + \dfrac{(6-7.07)^2}{7.07}$

$+ \dfrac{(21-18.96)^2}{18.96} + \dfrac{(16-13.84)^2}{13.84} + \dfrac{(11-9.82)^2}{9.82} + \dfrac{(23-26.34)^2}{26.34}$

$+ \dfrac{(6-7.2)^2}{7.2} + \dfrac{(5-5.11)^2}{5.11} + \dfrac{(15-13.7)^2}{13.7} = 1.7 \quad df = (3-1)(3-1) = 4$

Critical value: $\chi^2 = 9.488$. Decision: Fail to reject H_0. There is insufficient evidence to support the claim that the characteristics of belief about public funding of abortions and political affiliation are related.

13.17   (a) (i) $\chi^2 = 0$ (ii) $\chi^2 = 0$ (iii) $\chi^2 = 0$

(c) (i)

	B_1	B_2	B_3
A_1	20	10	30
A_2	60	30	90
A_3	180	90	270

(ii)

	B_1	B_2	B_3
A_1	20	10	30
A_2	60	30	90
A_3	30	15	45

13.18 H_0: The three populations are homogeneous with respect to proportion of women aged 20-24 who had ever married.

H_a: H_0 is not true.

$\alpha = 0.05$

Observed value: $\chi^2 = \sum \frac{(O-E)^2}{E} = \frac{(54-47.14)^2}{47.14} + \frac{(21-27.86)^2}{27.86}$

$+ \frac{(58-56.57)^2}{56.57} + \frac{(32-33.43)^2}{33.43} + \frac{(42-50.29)^2}{50.29} + \frac{(38-29.71)^2}{29.71} = 6.46$

$df = (3 - 1)(2 - 1) = 2$

Critical value: $\chi^2 = 5.991$. Decision: Reject H_0. The data indicate that the three populations are not homogeneous with respect to proportion of women aged 20-24 who had ever married.

13.19 H_0: The two dice are homogeneous with respect to the number of dots showing. H_a: H_0 is not true.

$\alpha = 0.05$.

Observed value: $\chi^2 = \sum \frac{(O-E)^2}{E} = \frac{(4-5.5)^2}{5.5} + \frac{(6-5)^2}{5} + \frac{(7-7.5)^2}{7.5}$

$+ \frac{(5-5.5)^2}{5.5} + \frac{(5-5)^2}{5} + \frac{(8-6.5)^2}{6.5} + \frac{(7-5.5)^2}{5.5} + \frac{(4-5)^2}{5} + \frac{(8-7.5)^2}{7.5}$

$+ \frac{(6-5.5)^2}{5.5} + \frac{(5-5)^2}{5} + \frac{(5-6.5)^2}{6.5} = 2.07$ $df = (2 - 1)(6 - 1) = 5$

Critical value: $\chi^2 = 11.071$. Decision: Fail to reject H_0. There is insufficient evidence to indicate that the two dice are not homogeneous with respect to number of dots showing.

13.20 H_0: The appropriate populations of medical doctors and student nurses are homogeneous with respect to smoking. H_a: H_0 is not true. $\alpha = 0.10$.

Observed value:

$$\chi^2 = \sum \frac{(O-E)^2}{E} = \frac{(18-15.56)^2}{15.56} + \frac{(32-34.44)^2}{34.44} + \frac{(10-12.44)^2}{12.44}$$

$$+ \frac{(30-27.56)^2}{27.56} = 1.25 \qquad\qquad df = (2-1)(2-1) = 1$$

Critical value: $\chi^2 = 2.706$. Decision: Fail to reject H_0. There is not sufficient evidence to indicate the populations of medical doctors and student nurses are not homogeneous with respect to smoking.

13.21 H_0: The appropriate populations of males and females are homogeneous with respect to belief of discrimination in salaries. H_a: H_0 is not true. $\alpha = 0.01$.

Observed value:

$$\chi^2 = \sum \frac{(O-E)^2}{E} = \frac{(55-65.22)^2}{65.22} + \frac{(70-59.78)^2}{59.78} + \frac{(65-54.78)^2}{54.78}$$

$$+ \frac{40-50.22)^2}{50.22} = 7.34 \qquad\qquad df = (2-1)(2-1) = 1$$

Critical value: $\chi^2 = 6.635$. Decision: Reject H_0. The data indicate that the populations of males and females are not homogeneous with respect to belief of discrimination in salaries.

13.22 H_0: The appropriate populations are homogeneous with respect to satisfaction of hospital care.
H_a: H_0 is not true. $\alpha = 0.05$.
Observed value: $\chi^2 = \sum \frac{(O-E)^2}{E} = \frac{(85-76.5)^2}{76.5} + \frac{(15-23.5)^2}{23.5} + \frac{(81-76.5)^2}{76.5}$

$$+ \frac{(19-23.5)^2}{23.5} + \frac{(70-76.5)^2}{76.5} + \frac{(30-23.5)^2}{23.5} + \frac{(68-76.5)^2}{76.5} + \frac{(32-23.5)^2}{23.5} = 11.4$$

$$df = (4-1)(2-1) = 3$$

Critical value: $\chi^2 = 7.815$. Decision: Reject H_0. The data indicate that the appropriate populations are not homogeneous with respect to satisfaction of hospital care.

13.24   (a)   0   (b)   (c)

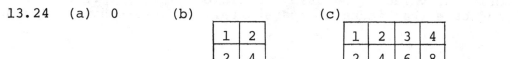

1	2
2	4

1	2	3	4
2	4	6	8

13.25 H_0: $p_A = 0.10$ $p_B = 0.20$ $p_C = 0.30$ $p_D = 0.25$ $p_F = 0.15$

H_a: H_0 is not true. $\alpha = 0.05$

Observed value: $\chi^2 = \sum \dfrac{(O-E)^2}{E} = \dfrac{(12-8)^2}{8} + \dfrac{(20-16)^2}{16} + \dfrac{(26-24)^2}{24}$

$+ \dfrac{(14-20)^2}{20} + \dfrac{(8-12)^2}{12} = 6.30$ df = 5 - 1 = 4

Critical value: $\chi^2 = 9.488$. Decision: Fail to reject H_0. The data do not suggest that the new teacher's grading policy is different from that of the department.

13.26 Let A, B, C, and D represent the categories less than or equal to -23.40, more than -23.40 but not more than 0, more than 0 but not more than 23.40, and more than 23.40 respectively. Using Table B-3, we obtain H_0. [For example, $P(x < -23.40) = P(z < -23.40/34.92) = P(z < -0.67) = 0.5 - 0.2486 = 0.2514$.]

H_0: $p_A = 0.2514$ $p_B = 0.2486$ $p_C = 0.2486$ $p_D = 0.2514$

H_a: H_0 is not true. $\alpha = 0.10$

Observed value: $\chi^2 = \sum \dfrac{(O-E)^2}{E} = \dfrac{(9-15.08)^2}{15.08} + \dfrac{(18-14.92)^2}{14.92}$

$+ \dfrac{(19-14.92)^2}{14.92} + \dfrac{(14-15.08)^2}{15.08} = 4.28$ df = 4 - 1 = 3

Critical value: $\chi^2 = 6.251$. Decision: Fail to reject H_0. There is insufficient evidence to conclude that the sampling is from a nonnormal population.

13.27 Let A, B, C, and D represent the categories drive alone, carpool, public transportation, and other means respectively.

H_0: $p_A = 0.70$ $p_B = 0.20$ $p_C = 0.08$ $p_D = 0.02$

H_a: H_0 is not true. $\alpha = 0.05$

Observed value: $\chi^2 = \sum \dfrac{(O-E)^2}{E} = \dfrac{(320-350)^2}{350} + \dfrac{(130-100)^2}{100}$

$+ \dfrac{(35-40)^2}{40} + \dfrac{(15-10)^2}{10} = 14.7$ df = 4 - 1 = 3

Critical value: $\chi^2 = 7.815$. Decision: Reject H_0. The data indicate that modes of transportation to work have changed.

13.28 H_0: The characteristics of political affiliation and
        attitude concerning racial quotas in hiring are
        independent.
      H_a: The characteristics of political affiliation and
        attitude concerning racial quotas in hiring are
        related.
      $\alpha = 0.05$

Observed value: $\chi^2 = \sum \dfrac{(O-E)^2}{E} = \dfrac{(7-6.29)^2}{6.29} + \dfrac{(7-5.11)^2}{5.11}$

$+ \dfrac{(9-11.6)^2}{11.6} + \dfrac{(19-19.15)^2}{19.15} + \dfrac{(13-15.56)^2}{15.56} + \dfrac{(38-35.3)^2}{35.3}$

$+ \dfrac{(6-6.56)^2}{6.56} + \dfrac{(6-5.33)^2}{5.33} + \dfrac{(12-12.1)^2}{12.1} = 2.12$

df $= (3-1)(3-1) = 4$

Critical value: $\chi^2 = 9.488$. Decision: Fail to reject H_0.
The data do not indicate that the characteristics of
political affiliation and attitude concerning racial
quotas in hiring are related.

13.29 H_0: The characteristics of gender and CHD are independent.
      H_a: The characteristics of gender and CHD are related.
      $\alpha = 0.10$

Observed value: $\chi^2 = \sum \dfrac{(O-E)^2}{E} = \dfrac{(54-51.6)^2}{51.6} + \dfrac{(32-34.4)^2}{34.4}$

$+ \dfrac{(39-41.4)^2}{41.4} + \dfrac{(30-27.6)^2}{27.6} = 0.63 \qquad$ df $= (2-1)(2-1) = 1$

Critical value: $\chi^2 = 2.706$. Decision: Fail to reject H_0.
The data do not indicate that the characteristics of
gender and CHD are related.

13.30 H_0: The characteristics of starting time and means of
        transportation to work are independent.
      H_a: The characteristics of starting time and means of
        transportation to work are related.
      $\alpha = 0.01$

Observed value: $\chi^2 = \sum \dfrac{(O-E)^2}{E} = \dfrac{(65-75.52)^2}{75.52} + \dfrac{(39-30.68)^2}{30.68} + \dfrac{(10-8.26)^2}{8.26} + \dfrac{(4-3.54)^2}{3.54}$

$+ \dfrac{(95-100.48)^2}{100.48} + \dfrac{(45-40.82)^2}{40.82} + \dfrac{(11-10.99)^2}{10.99} + \dfrac{(6-4.71)^2}{4.71} + \dfrac{(160-144)^2}{144} + \dfrac{(46-58.5)^2}{58.5}$

$+ \dfrac{(14-15.75)^2}{15.75} + \dfrac{(5-6.75)^2}{6.75} = 10.33 \qquad$ df $= (3-1)(4-1) = 6$

Critical value: $\chi^2 = 16.812$. Decision: Fail to reject H_0.

13.30 Continued:

The data do not indicate that the characteristics of starting time and means of transportation to work are related.

13.31 H_0: The appropriate male and female populations are homogeneous with respect to age.
H_a: H_0 is not true. $\alpha = 0.05$

Observed value: $\chi^2 = \sum \dfrac{(O-E)^2}{E} = \dfrac{(45-36.43)^2}{36.43} + \dfrac{(20-25.71)^2}{25.71}$

$+ \dfrac{(10-12.86)^2}{12.86} + \dfrac{(40-48.57)^2}{48.57} + \dfrac{(40-34.29)^2}{34.29} + \dfrac{(20-17.14)^2}{17.14} = 6.86$

df $= (2-1)(3-1) = 2$

Critical value: $\chi^2 = 5.991$. Decision: Reject H_0. There is sufficient evidence to indicate that the appropriate male and female populations are not homogeneous with respect to age.

13.32 H_0: The characteristics of means of transportation to work are homogeneous with respect to sex.
H_a: H_0 is not true. $\alpha = 0.01$

Observed value: $\chi^2 = \sum \dfrac{(O-E)^2}{E} = \dfrac{(173-160)^2}{160} + \dfrac{(58-65)^2}{65}$

$+ \dfrac{(15-17.5)^2}{17.5} + \dfrac{(4-7.5)^2}{7.5} + \dfrac{(147-160)^2}{160} + \dfrac{(72-65)^2}{65} + \dfrac{(20-17.5)^2}{17.5}$

$+ \dfrac{(11-7.5)^2}{7.5} = 7.6$ df $= (2-1)(4-1) = 3$

Critical value: $\chi^2 = 11.345$. Decision: Fail to reject H_0. The data do not indicate that the characteristics of means of transportation to work and sex are homogeneous.

13.33 (a) H_0: The attitude concerning racial quotas in hiring are homogeneous with respect to appropriate populations of Democrats, Republicans, and Independents.

H_a: H_0 is not true.

(b) Same.

14.1 (a) {0,1,2,10,11,12}   (b) 0.063   (c) {0,1,2}

(d) 0.07 (e) {11,12,13,14,15}   (f) 0.047

(g) {0,1,2,3,4,5}   (h) 0.032   (i) 0.124   (j) 0.031

(k) {0,1,2,3,4,12,13,14,15,16}   (ℓ) {14,15,16,17,18,19}

14.2 H_0: Md $\geq$ 30 H_a: Md < 30   Test statistic and observed
value: Let x be the number of data values larger than 30.
So x = 3.
Critical region = {0,1,2}, n = 11, α = 0.005 + 0.027 = 0.032.
Decision: Fail to reject H_0. The data do not support
the runner's claim.

14.3 H_0: Md $\leq$ 2.8 H_a: Md > 2.8   Test statistic and observed
value: Let x be the number of data values larger than
2.8. So x = 8.
Critical region = {8,9,10}, n = 10, α = 0.044 + 0.010 + 0.001
= 0.055. Decision: Reject H_0. The data indicate that
the median time is larger than 2.8.

14.4 (a) H_0: Md $\geq$ 20 H_a: Md < 20
Test statistic and observed value: Let x be the number
of data values larger than 20. So x = 5.
Critical region = {0,1,2,3}, n = 13, α = 0.002 + 0.010
+ 0.035 = 0.047. Decision: Fail to reject H_0. There
is insufficient evidence to support the claim.

(b) Test statistic: $z = \dfrac{x - n/2}{\sqrt{n}/2} = \dfrac{15 - 39/2}{\sqrt{39}/2} = -1.44$

Critical value: z = -1.65. Decision: Fail to reject
H_0.

14.5 H_0: Md $\leq$ 0 H_a: Md > 0

Test statistic and observed value: Let x be the number of
differences (weight before-weight after) larger than 0.
So x = 6.
Critical region = {7,8}, n = 8, α = 0.031 + 0.004 = 0.035
Decision: Fail to reject H_0. The data do not indicate
that the diet is effective.

14.6

	Critical value	Decision
(a)	2	Fail to reject H_0
(b)	1	Fail to reject H_0
(c)	2	Reject H_0
(d)	2	Fail to reject H_0
(e)	6	Reject H_0
(f)	5	Reject H_0
(g)	11	Fail to reject H_0
(h)	30	Reject H_0
(i)	24	Reject H_0
(j)	60	Fail to reject H_0

14.7 (a)

Sample data x	Difference D=x-10	Magnitude $\lvert D \rvert$	Signed rank
18	8	8	6
12	2	2	1
4	-6	6	-4
1	-9	9	-7
15	5	5	3
17	7	7	5
26	16	16	9
0	-10	10	-8
14	4	4	2

(b) H_0: Md $\leq$ 10 H_a: Md > 10 $\alpha = 0.05$

Observed value: $W^- = 4 + 7 + 8 = 19$
Critical value: c = 8. Decision: Fail to reject H_0.

14.8 (a)

Sample data x	Difference D=x-60	Magnitude $\lvert D \rvert$	Signed rank
49	−11	11	−6
54	− 6	6	−3
68	8	8	4
72	12	12	7
65	5	5	2
51	−9	9	−5
45	−15	15	−8
58	−2	2	−1

(b) H_0: Md $= 60$ H_a: Md $\neq 60$ $\alpha = 0.10$

$W^- = 6 + 5 + 3 + 8 + 1 = 23$ $W^+ = 4 + 7 + 2 = 13$

Observed value: $W = 13$ Critical value: $c = 6$
Decision: Fail to reject H_0.

14.9 (a)

Sample data x	Difference D=x-50	Magnitude $\lvert D \rvert$	Signed rank
42	−8	8	−4
39	−11	11	−5
37	−13	13	−6
55	5	5	3
46	−4	4	−2
52	2	2	1
33	−17	17	−7

(b) H_0: Md ≥ 50 H_a: Md < 50 $\alpha = 0.05$

Observed value: $W^+ = 3 + 1 = 4$.   Critical value: $c = 4$.
Decision: Reject H_0.

14.10 The data are expressed in thousands of dollars.

H_0: Md $= 30$ H_a: Md $\neq 30$ $\alpha = 0.05$

Data (x)	28.9	31.5	42.5	28	34.9	32.5	36.9	38.5	37.9	32.9
D=x-30	−1.1	1.5	12.5	−2	4.9	2.5	6.9	8.5	7.9	2.9
Signed rank	−1	2	10	−3	6	4	7	9	8	5

$W^- = 4$, $W^+ = 51$ Observed value: $W = 4$.   Critical value: $c = 8$.
Decision: Reject H_0.   The data do not support the
salesman's claim.

14.11 H_0: Md $\leq$ 10 H_a: Md > 10 $\alpha = 0.01$

Data (x)	10.3	9.2	10.6	11.1	9.5	12	12.2	9.1	10.7	13.1	12.1
D=x-10	0.3	-0.8	0.6	1.1	-0.5	2	2.2	-0.9	0.7	3.1	2.1
Signed rank	3	-7	5	10	-4	12	14	-8	6	15	13

Data (x)	10.1	10.2	11.3	11
D=x-10	0.1	0.2	1.3	1
Signed rank	1	2	11	9

Observed value: $W^- = 7 + 4 + 8 = 19$. Critical value: $c = 20$.
Decision: Reject H_0. The data do not support the claim that
the lotion relieves the symptom within 10 minutes.

14.12 H_0: Md $\geq$ 3 H_a: Md < 3 $\alpha = 0.05$

Data (x)	2.7	3.4	3.2	1.8	2.5	2.4	4	2.3	2.2	3.1	1.1	1.5
D=x-3	-0.3	0.4	0.2	-1.2	-0.5	-0.6	1	-0.7	-0.8	0.1	-1.9	-1.5
Signed rank	-3	4	2	-10	-5	-6	9	-7	-8	1	-12	-11

Observed value: $W^+ = 4 + 2 + 9 + 1 = 16$. Critical value: $c = 17$.
Decision: Reject H_0. The data indicate that the median time
before servicing is required is less than 3 years.

14.13 H_0: Md $\leq$ 520 H_a: Md > 520 $\alpha = 0.01$

Data (x)	535	560	500	550	560	540	610	490	545	550	510
D=x-520	15	40	-20	30	40	20	90	-30	25	30	-10
Signed rank	3	11.5	-4.5	8	11.5	4.5	16	-8	6	8	-2

Data (x)	620	460	575	485	630	600	515	640	650
D=x-520	100	-60	55	-35	110	80	-5	120	130
Signed rank	17	-14	13	-10	18	15	-1	19	20

Observed value: $W^- = 4.5 + 8 + 2 + 14 + 10 + 1 = 39.5$
Critical value: $c = 43$. Decision: Reject H_0. The data
indicate that the advertising campaign was successful.

14.14   Let D = weight before-weight after.

(a) H_0: $Md_D \leq 0$ H_a: $Md_D > 0$ $\alpha = 0.05$

D	5	-4	7	-2	11	3	6	5
Signed rank	4.5	-3	7	-1	8	2	6	4.5

Observed value: $W^- = 3 + 1 = 4$. Critical value: $c = 6$.
Decision: Reject H_0.

14.14 (b) In exercise 14.5, the sign test was used to test the claim. The decision was fail to reject H_0.

(c) The Wilcoxon signed-rank test is a more sensitive test than the sign test.

14.15 Let $D = x_1 - x_2$ be expressed in tens.

(a) H_0: $Md_D \geq 0$ H_a: $Md_D < 0$ $\alpha = 0.05$

D	1	-2	-7	4	5	-3	-14	10	13	11	-2	8	-16
Signed rank	1.5	-4	-11	8	9	-6.5	-19	15.5	18	17	-4	12.5	-21

	-19	-3	10	-23	-15	2	-21	-8	-9	-18	-17	-1	-6
	-24	-6.5	15.5	-26	-20	4	-25	-12.5	-14	-23	-22	-1.5	-10

Observed value: $W^+ = 1.5+8+9+15.5+18+17+12.5+15.5+4 = 101$
Critical value: $c = 110$. Decision: Reject H_0. The data indicate that judge A tends to give lower performance ratings than judge B.

(b) $\mu_W = n(n + 1)/4 = (26)(27)/4 = 175.5$

$$\sigma_W = \sqrt{\frac{n(n+1)(2n+1)}{24}} = \sqrt{\frac{(26)(27)(53)}{24}} = 39.37$$

Observed value: $z = \dfrac{101 - 175.5}{39.37} = -1.89$

Critical value: $z = -1.65$. Decision: Reject H_0.

14.16

	Critical value	Decision
(a)	11	Fail to reject H_0
(b)	21	Reject H_0
(c)	90	Reject H_0
(d)	31	Fail to reject H_0
(e)	45	Reject H_0
(f)	44	Fail to reject H_0
(g)	1	Fail to reject H_0
(h)	60	Reject H_0
(i)	7	Reject H_0

14.17 (a)

x	Rank (x)	y	Rank (y)
43	1	55	4
47	2	62	6
51	3	68	8
59	5	75	10
65	7		
71	9		
Sums:	27		28

(b) $H_0: Md_x = Md_y$ $H_a: Md_x \neq Md_y$ $\alpha = 0.10$

$$U_x = 27 - \frac{(6)(7)}{2} = 6 \qquad U_y = 28 - \frac{4(5)}{2} = 18$$

Observed value: $U = U_x = 6$. Critical value: $c = 3$
Decision: Fail to reject H_0.

14.18 (a)

x	Rank (x)	y	Rank (y)
33	4	20	1
36	6	23	2
42	8	28	3
45	9	34	5
49	10	37	7
Sums:	37		18

(b) $H_0: Md_x \leq Md_y$ $H_a: Md_x > Md_y$ $\alpha = 0.05$

Observed value: $U = U_y = 18 - \frac{(5)(6)}{2} = 3$
Critical value: $c = 4$. Decision: Reject H_0.

14.19 $H_0: Md_x \geq Md_y$ $H_a: Md_x < Md_y$ $\alpha = 0.05$

Data	13.6	13.9	14.5	14.7	15.2	15.3	16.1	17.2	17.3	17.5
	x	x	y	x	x	x	y	x	y	y
Ranks	1	2	3	4	5	6	7	8	9	10

Data	17.9	18.1	18.4	19.2	20.5
	y	x	y	y	y
Ranks	11	12	13	14	15

$S_x = 1 + 2 + 4 + 5 + 6 + 8 + 12 = 38$
Observed value: $U = U_x = 38 - \frac{7(8)}{2} = 10$.

Critical value: $c = 13$. Decision: Reject H_0. The data support the claim that the median endurance level of soccer players is larger than for football players.

14.20 H_0: $Md_x = Md_y$ H_a: $Md_x \neq Md_y$ $\alpha = 0.10$

Data	68	71	73	77	80	85	90	92	97	101	106	108
	y	y	y	x	x	x	x	x	y	y	y	y
Ranks	1	2	3	4	5	6	7	8	9	10	11	12

$S_x = 4 + 5 + 6 + 7 + 8 = 30$

$S_y = 1 + 2 + 3 + 9 + 10 + 11 + 12 = 48$

$U_x = 30 - \dfrac{5(6)}{2} = 15$ $U_y = 48 - \dfrac{7(8)}{2} = 20$

Observed value: $U = U_x = 15$. Critical value: $\bar{c} = 6$.
Decision: Fail to reject H_0. There is not sufficient
evidence to indicate a difference in the median cost.

14.21 H_0: $Md_x \leq Md_y$ H_a: $Md_x > Md_y$ $\alpha = 0.05$

Data	34.7	34.9	35.8	36.2	36.3	36.5	36.6	36.8	36.9	37.1	37.3	37.5
	y	y	y	x	y	x	y	y	x	y	x	y
Ranks	1	2	3	4	5	6	7	8	9	10	11	12

Data	37.6	37.7	37.9	38.0	38.2	38.3	38.5	38.8
	x	x	x	y	y	x	x	x
Ranks	13	14	15	16	17	18	19	20

$S_y = 1 + 2 + 3 + 5 + 7 + 8 + 10 + 12 + 16 + 17 = 81$

Observed value: $U = U_y = 81 - \dfrac{10(11)}{2} = 26$

Critical value: $c = 27$. Decision: Reject H_0. The data
support the claim that brand y tends to get better gas
mileage than brand x.

14.22 (a) H_0: $Md_x = Md_y$ H_a: $Md_x \neq Md_y$ $\alpha = 0.05$

Data	34	40	52	54	55	58	59	62	63	64	67	68	70
	y	x	y	x	x	y	x	x	y	x	x	y	y
Ranks	1	2	3	4	5	6	7	8	9	10	11	12	13

Data	71	73	76	77	78	79	84	86	88	89	90	91	92	95
	y	y	y	x	x	y	y	y	x	y	x	x	x	y
Ranks	14	15	16	17	18	19	20	21	22	23	24	25	26	27

14.22 (a) Continued:

$$S_x = 2+4+5+7+8+10+11+17+18+22+24+25+26 = 179$$

$$S_y = 1+3+6+9+12+13+14+15+16+19+20+21+23+27 = 199$$

$$U_x = 179 - \frac{13(14)}{2} = 88 \qquad U_y = 199 - \frac{14(15)}{2} = 94$$

Observed value: $U = U_x = 88$. Critical value: $c = 50$.

Decision: Fail to reject H_0. The data do not dispute the chairperson's claim.

(b) $\mu_U = \frac{(13)(14)}{2} = 91 \qquad \sigma_U = \sqrt{\frac{(13)(14)(13+14+1)}{12}} = 20.61$

Observed value: $z = \frac{88-91}{20.61} = -0.15$

Critical values: $z = \pm 1.96$. Decision: Fail to reject H_0.

14.23

	c_1	c_2	R	Decision
(a)	2	9	2	Reject H_0
(b)	3	11	12	Reject H_0
(c)	3	12	4	Fail to reject H_0
(d)	3	11	8	Fail to reject H_0
(e)	3	12	7	Fail to reject H_0
(f)	4	13	9	Fail to reject H_0

14.24 H_0: The process is random H_a: The process is not random.
$$\alpha = 0.05$$

Observed value: $R = 4$.

Critical values: $c_1 = 3$, $c_2 = 10$ ($n_1 = 4$, $n_2 = 8$)

Decision: Fail to reject H_0. There is not enough evidence to indicate that the process is not random.

14.25 H_0: The process is random. H_a: The process is not random
$$\alpha = 0.05$$

Observed value: $R = 3$.

Critical values: $c_1 = 2$, $c_2 = 8$ ($n_1 = 3$, $n_2 = 12$)

Decision: Fail to reject H_0. The data do not indicate that the process is not random.

14.26 (a) H_0: The process is random $\quad H_a$: The process is not random

$$\alpha = 0.05$$

Observed value: $R = 9$

Critical values: $c_1 = 8$, $c_2 = 19$ $\quad (n_1 = 11, n_2 = 14)$

Decision: Fail to reject H_0. The data do not indicate that the process is not random.

(b) $\mu_R = \dfrac{2(11)(14)}{11 + 14} + 1 = 13.32$

$$\sigma_R = \sqrt{\dfrac{2(11)(14)[2(11)(14) - 11 - 14]}{(11 + 14)^2(11 + 14 - 1)}} = 2.41$$

Observed value: $z = \dfrac{9 - 13.32}{2.41} = -1.79$

Critical values: $z = \pm 1.96$. Decision: Fail to reject H_0.

14.27 (a) H_0: Md ≤ 425 $\quad H_a$: Md > 425

Let x be the number of data values larger than 425.
Observed value: $x = 13$.
Critical region: $\{14,15,16,17,18,19,20\}$, $\quad n = 20$
$\alpha = 0.037 + 0.015 + 0.005 + 0.001 = 0.058$

Decision: Fail to reject H_0.

(b)

Data (x)	435	460	470	415	420	460	400	410	500	475
D=x-425	10	35	45	-10	-5	35	-25	-15	75	50
Signed rank	3	13.5	16.5	-3	-1	13.5	-10	-5.5	20	18

Data (x)	415	405	450	400	465	470	445	440	455	480
D=x-425	-10	-20	25	-25	40	45	20	15	30	55
Signed rank	-3	-7.5	10	-10	15	16.5	7.5	5.5	12	19

Observed value: $W^- = 3 + 1 + 10 + 5.5 + 3 + 7.5 + 10 = 40$
Critical value: $c = 60$ $\quad (\alpha = 0.05)$
Decision: Reject H_0.

(c) The Wilcoxon signed-rank test is a more sensitive test than the sign test.

14.28 (a) H_0: Md $= 9.3$ H_a: Md $\neq 9.3$

Let x be the number of data values larger than 9.3.
Observed value: $x = 8$. Critical region: $\{0,1,9,10\}$, $n = 10$,
$\alpha = (0.001 + 0.010)2 = 0.022$. Decision: Fail to reject H_0.

(b)

Data (x)	9.6	9.8	9.1	10.2	10.1	9.8	8.5	10.3	9.9	10.0
D=x-9.3	0.3	0.5	-0.2	0.9	0.8	0.4	-0.8	1	0.6	0.7
Signed rank	2	4	-1	9	7.5	3	-7.5	10	5	6

$W^+ = 2+4+9+7.5+3+10+5+6 = 46.5$ $W^- = 1 + 7.5 = 8.5$

Observed value: $W = W^- = 8.5$.
Critical value: $c = 8$ ($\alpha = 0.05$). Decision: Fail to reject H_0.

14.29 (a) H_0: Md ≥ 200 H_a: Md < 200

Let x be the number of data values larger than 200.
Observed value: $x = 2$.
Critical region: $\{0,1\}$, $n=8$, $\alpha=0.004 + 0.031 = 0.035$
Decision: Fail to reject H_0.

(b)

Data (x)	193	203	196	192	187	206	190	195
D=x-200	-7	3	-4	-8	-13	6	-10	-5
Signed rank	-5	1	-2	-6	-8	4	-7	-3

Observed value: $W^+ = 1 + 4 = 5$.
Critical value: $c = 6$ ($\alpha = 0.05$) Decision: Reject H_0.

(c) The Wilcoxon signed-rank test is a more sensitive
test than the sign test.

14.30 H_0: Md ≤ 425 H_a: Md > 425 $\alpha = 0.05$

$\mu_W = 20(21)/4 = 105$. $\sigma_W = \sqrt{\dfrac{20(21)(41)}{24}} = 26.79$

Observed value: $z = \dfrac{40 - 105}{26.79} = -2.43$. Critical value:
$z = -1.65$.
Decision: Reject H_0. The data indicate that the median
rent is more than $425.
Note: From Exercise 14.27 we have $W^- = 40$.

14.31 $H_0: Md_x \geq Md_y$ $H_a: Md_x < Md_y$ $\alpha = 0.05$

Data	40	45	55	57	65	70	71	72	74	76	77	78	82	84	88	92
	x	x	y	x	x	x	x	x	x	y	y	y	y	x	y	y
Ranks	1	2	3	4	5	6	7	8	9	10	11	12	13	14	15	16

$S_x = 1 + 2 + 4 + 5 + 6 + 7 + 8 + 9 + 14 = 56$

Observed value: $U = U_x = 56 - \dfrac{(9)(10)}{2} = 11$

Critical value: c = 15. Decision: Reject H_0. The data support the teacher's claim.

14.32 $H_0: Md_x = Md_y$ $H_a: Md_x \neq Md_y$ $\alpha = 0.10$

Data	7.4	7.5	7.8	8.0	8.2	8.5	8.7	8.8	8.9
	x	x	y	x	y	y	x	y	y
Ranks	1	2	3	4	5	6	7	8	9

$S_x = 1 + 2 + 4 + 7 = 14$ $S_y = 3 + 5 + 6 + 8 + 9 = 31$

$U_x = 14 - \dfrac{4(5)}{2} = 4$ $U_y = 31 - \dfrac{5(6)}{2} = 16$

Observed value: $U = U_x = 4$. Critical value: c = 2.

Decision: Fail to reject H_0. The data do not indicate that the population medians are different.

14.33 Let x and y represent resorts A and B respectively.
$H_0: Md_x \geq Md_y$ $H_a: Md_x < Md_y$ $\alpha = 0.01$

Data	30.9	32.5	35	36	39.5	40.9	42.5	44.3	47.9	48.9	53.9	61
	x	x	x	y	x	y	y	x	y	x	y	y
Ranks	1	2	3	4	5	6	7	8	9	10	11	12

$S_x = 1 + 2 + 3 + 5 + 8 + 10 = 29$.

Observed value: $U = U_x = 29 - \dfrac{6(7)}{2} = 8$. Critical value: c = 3.

Decision: Fail to reject H_0. The data do not support the claim that the median price of building lots is less in town A.

14.34 H_0: The process is random H_a: The process is not random

  $\alpha = 0.05$

  Observed value: $R = 9$.   Critical values: $c_1 = 4$, $c_2 = 13$

  $(n_1 = 8,\ n_2 = 7)$

  Decision: Fail to reject H_0. The data do not indicate
  that the process is not random.

14.35 (a) H_0: The process is random H_a: The process is not
    random

    $\alpha = 0.05$

    Observed value: $R = 8$.
    Critical values: $c_1 = 8$, $c_2 = 19$ $(n_1 = 12,\ n_2 = 13)$.
    Decision: Reject H_0. The data indicate a lack of
    randomness.

  (b) $\mu_R = \dfrac{2(12)(13)}{12 + 13} + 1 = 13.48$

    $\sigma_R = \sqrt{\dfrac{2(12)(13)[2(12)(13) - 12 - 13]}{(12 + 13)^2(12 + 13 - 1)}} = 2.44$

    Observed value: $z = \dfrac{8 - 13.48}{2.44} = -2.25$

    Critical values: $z = \pm 1.96$. Decision: Reject H_0.

14.36 H_0: $Md_x \le Md_y$ H_a: $Md_x > Md_y$ $\alpha = 0.05$

  $\mu_U = (10)(10)/2 = 50$ $\sigma_U = \sqrt{(10)(10)(10+10+1) \div 12} = 13.23$

    Observed value: $z = \dfrac{26-50}{\sqrt{175}} = -1.81$

    Critical value: $z = -1.65$

    Decision: Reject H_0